Ireland

Ireland

Photographs by Marc Berger
Text by Richard Killeen

Gill & Macmillan

Cover:
A view of Long Strand Bay near Galley Head.

Frontispiece:
The Rock of Cashel was both an ancient royal
site and a medieval monastic and episcopal
centre. It rises dramatically from the plains of
County Tipperary.

Page 5:
Near Ventry on the Dingle Peninsula; County
Kerry.

Page 6:
The monastic site at Glendalough is in the heart
of the Wicklow Mountains, yet it is only an
hour's drive from the centre of Dublin. Founded
in the 7th century by St Kevin, it has always been
a place of pilgrimage. This photograph shows
the round tower and St Kevin's Church.

Published in Ireland by
Gill & Macmillan Ltd
Goldenbridge
Dublin 8
with associated companies throughout the world
© Artcolor Verlag GmbH, Hamm/Westf. und Leipzig 1997
0 7171 2602 1
Printed in Germany

A catalogue record for this book is available from the British Library.

Contents

History   7

The Provinces   17

Irish Writers   42

Dublin   54

Map   76

Glossary   77

The Authors   79

Select Bibliography   79

History

To Homer, writing in the 8th century b.c., all of north-west Europe was "a land of fog and gloom". The mysterious ocean that lay beyond was "the Sea of Death, where Hell begins". This forbidding region, so far from the warmth and civilization of the classical world, was unknown to the Greeks and feared like all unknown things.

The Romans did better. They conquered all of the continental land mass west of the Rhine and most of the island of Britain. They introduced the uniformity of imperial rule, the Latin language and – in later centuries – the new state religion of the empire, Christianity. To a Roman legionnaire, Britain must have seemed like the end of the earth.

But it was not. To the west, there lay another large island known to the Romans. They called it Hibernia: winter land. Although they traded with it and some of them almost certainly visited it, they never settled there. It was too remote, not important enough. Yet this island had supported human life in one form or another for over 7,000 years before the Romans conquered Britain. This island, the last significant European land mass before one reaches the vastness of the Atlantic Ocean, is known to us as Ireland.

Celtic Origins

Ireland was always the most remote part of Western Europe. It still is. With the opening of the Channel Tunnel between Britain and France, it is now the only member state of the European Union without a direct land link to the rest of the community. Yet it has been inhabited almost since the end of the Ice Age. Indeed, one of the oldest recorded sites of human habitation in all of Europe has been excavated at Mount Sandel, in Co. Derry. Archaeologists have dated it to 5935 b.c.

Together with Scotland, Wales, Brittany and Cornwall in south-west England, Ireland is spoken of as part of the Celtic world. But the Celts did not arrive in Ireland until about 250 b.c. Before that, there was a succession of pre-Celtic peoples who have left us a rich archaeological legacy. None of these is more impressive or spectacular than Newgrange, a large passage grave in the Boyne Valley, Co. Meath. Newgrange dates from the time of the great Egyptian pyramids and is proof of the sophistication and organisation of the people who built it.

But eventually the Celts arrived and swept all before them. They established a uniform culture throughout the island. There was a common language, Gaelic, which has survived until modern times and is still spoken by a minority of Irish people. Today, it is usually called Irish rather than Gaelic and is one of the two official languages of the Republic of Ireland (the other is obviously English). Celtic Ireland also had a common currency, based on the value of cattle and a common legal system. What it lacked was a strong political centre. There was no unitary authority. Instead, the island was divided into over 150 petty kingdoms, all contending for power, influence, territory and wealth. There were constant disputes, raids and local wars.

Influential Christianity

The Celts were a pastoral people. They built no towns. But with the coming of Christianity in the 5th century there soon developed monasteries which served as centres of piety and scholarship. They were not trading centres, however, nor did they have any commercial function. That sort of urban settlement had to await the arrival of the Vikings in the late 8th century. Clonmacnoise, by the banks of the River Shannon in Co. Offaly, is probably the best known of the early monastic settlements.

St Patrick, the national saint of Ireland, was a Roman Briton who had been captured by Irish pirates as a young man and sold into slavery in Co. Antrim. After seven years, he escaped and returned to Britain and eventually became a priest. In a dream, he heard the people of Ireland calling him back to evangelise them. He did so. His mission dates from 431; this is usually taken as the foundation date for Irish Christianity.

The new religion was an immediate success, establishing itself throughout the entire island. Of course, it adapted to its surroundings. Celtic Christianity absorbed some traditional practices which were opposed to orthodox church teaching, such as divorce. It also differed socially from continental norms, because the absence of towns meant that it was

The dense woods of Glendalough surround the great round tower. Glendalough, which in Irish means "the valley of the two lakes", is flanked on both sides by high, wooded hills. The monastic site lies in the area between the lakes.

impossible to establish bishoprics; instead, the monasteries served as Ireland's religious centres.

The heroic age of Irish Christianity was the period from the 6th to the 9th centuries. In that time, Irish missionaries travelled throughout Europe spreading the gospel. The Christian church had suffered like all Roman institutions following the collapse of the empire, as the continent entered the so-called Dark Ages. Only in Ireland, safe by virtue of its remoteness and the fact that it had never been part of the Roman world, was the church strong and vigorous. So, by a great irony, it fell to the missionaries from distant Ireland to re-evangelise the Christian heartland.

Survivals of this great early missionary effort are still visible in Europe today. St Columbanus founded the great monasteries at Luxeuil in France and Bobbio in northern Italy; St Gallen in Switzerland is named for St Gall. St Fergal (in Latin, Virgil) was bishop of Salzburg in the second half of the 8th century and Irish missionaries were recorded as far afield as Sicily and Kiev. John Scotus Eriugena, an Irishman and a former student at Clonmacnoise, was the leading philosopher at the court of Charlemagne.

In Ireland itself, there are many survivals from the early Christian era, from the ruins of monastic sites like Clonmacnoise or Glendalough, Co. Wicklow, with their distinctive round towers, to the superb illuminated manuscripts made by the monks. Of these, the most famous by far is the Book of Kells, a version of the Gospels, which may be seen in the library of Trinity College, Dublin.

Norman Conquerors

This self-contained world was severely disrupted by the arrival of the first Viking longships off the Irish coast in 795 a.d. The Vikings sought to plunder the wealthy Irish monasteries. But they were also traders and, like all traders, they needed permanent settlements. These became the first proper Irish towns: Dublin, Cork, Waterford, Limerick and Wexford all owe their origins to the Vikings.

In time, the Vikings came to coexist with Gaelic Ireland through trade, alliances and inter-marriage. The Gaelic world, meanwhile, was moving very slowly towards some form of political unity. In the early 11th century, King Brian Boru briefly managed to assert an effective claim to the High Kingship of Ireland. But this claim did not survive his death at the Battle of Clontarf in 1014.

After that, the old ways resumed although many powerful regional kings dreamt of emulating Brian Boru's example. Then, in 1169, the Anglo-Normans arrived. The original Normans had been Viking settlers in Normandy and had been absorbed into the wider Carolingian world of modern France and Germany. They had conquered England in 1066. They came to Ireland at the invitation of one of the Gaelic sub-kings to assist him in a local dispute. With amazing speed, the Normans swept across the island, establishing themselves in most parts outside central and western Ulster. They were formidable soldiers, much more advanced in their military technology than the native Irish. In addition, they had building skills on a scale never before seen in Ireland; thus, they were able to construct enormous fortresses like Carrickfergus Castle, Co. Antrim, or King John's Castle in Limerick. All over the countryside, they built tall, fortified tower houses to defend the lands they had won.

The Normans were subjects of the kings of England. Naturally, King Henry II was not going to allow them a free hand in Ireland, so he crossed the Irish Sea in 1172 to extract pledges of loyalty from them, as well as from many Gaelic kings, and to proclaim himself Lord of Ireland. He was the first English king to claim jurisdiction over Ireland. Then he went back to England, never to return.

This set the pattern for medieval Ireland. The English king was far away. All of Norman Ireland and much of Gaelic Ireland acknowledged his lordship. But within Ireland, there was a constant contest for power. Usually, the Norman settlers held the upper hand, although there was a revival of Gaelic fortunes in the 14th century. In addition, the Normans themselves often adopted Gaelic ways. By the late medieval period, two great Norman families – the FitzGeralds and the Butlers – controlled most of Ireland through vast land holdings, marriage alliances and their connections at the English court.

The oratorium at Newgrange.

English Triumph

All this changed quite suddenly in the early 16th century. The Reformation came to England and King Henry VIII tried to centralise his kingdom. In Ireland, he broke the power of the great Norman families and sought instead to rule through viceroys and deputies sent over from London. The English also tried to introduce Protestantism into Ireland, but failed.

Both the Normans and the Gaelic people remained Catholic. The problem for the English was simple. England had quickly become a Protestant power. It was the European norm for religious uniformity to exist within states, yet Ireland – which England now claimed – was still robustly Catholic.

In addition to this religious dilemma, there was the fact that effective English rule in Ireland was very difficult to achieve. In Ulster – large parts of which had never been touched by the Normans – the old Gaelic kingdoms still reigned supreme. In many other parts, Norman and Gaelic lords alike resented the creeping centralisation of the English regime based on the capital, Dublin.

In effect, it took 150 years of sporadic conflict to resolve these issues. First, the Gaelic kingdoms of Ulster were destroyed in the late 16th century. The lands that were conquered were settled by imported English and Scots planters, all of them Protestants. The terrible campaign of Oliver Cromwell in the southern half of the island in the late 1640s was followed by a vast confiscation of land.

Most Catholic landowners – whether from a Norman or a Gaelic background – were dispossessed. In their place, a new class of English settler was established. This group of people, later known as the Protestant Ascendancy, formed the majority of Irish landowners until the early 20th century.

By the start of the 18th century, peace had returned. Ireland was formally a sister kingdom of England. In reality, it was an English colony. The tiny Ascendancy class held supreme control; the Catholic majority was excluded from power, land and political and military office. Even in Ulster, where the local Protestant majority was Calvinist rather than Anglican, the rule of the Anglican Ascendancy was supreme.

The 18th century was the golden age of this Ascendancy. Secure in their power, they built fine country houses and beautiful towns. Much still survives, especially in Dublin, which they turned from a dull backwater into a splendid European city.

The tide of revolution which swept across Europe after 1789 had a profound effect in Ireland. The republican idea took hold. In Ulster, it appealed to some radical Calvinists who resented the ascendancy of the Anglicans. Indeed, some dissident Anglicans also became enthusiastic republicans, most famously Theobald Wolfe Tone. Republicanism also had an appeal to the Catholic masses who hoped that revolutionary France would liberate them from the English rule.

Revolutionary Times

The rebellion of 1798 was the product of this ferment. The main rising occurred in the south-east and lasted for over a month. A smaller outbreak in Ulster was quickly contained. Finally, a tiny French force landed in the west in the autumn and, after some initial success, was forced to surrender. In all, over 30,000 people died in 1798. In reaction to these events, the Irish colonial parliament was abolished in 1800 and Ireland was wholly absorbed into the United Kingdom.

Prosperity and Destitution in the 19th Century

In the 19th century, three forces dominated Ireland: nationalism, industrialisation and famine. Nationalism became in effect the demand by Irish Catholics for autonomy of one sort or another. Radicals among them looked to the republican tradition of 1798 and sought complete independence. The moderate majority, under the leadership first of Daniel O'Connell and later of Charles Stewart Parnell, were prepared to settle for domestic home rule within the United Kingdom, rather like the Austro-Hungarian "ausgleich" of 1867.

The industrial revolution left Ireland untouched, except for Ulster. There, the economy was transformed by linen and shipbuilding. North-east Ulster became, in effect, a part of the greater industrial economy of north-west Britain and Belfast a city like Manchester, Birmingham or Glasgow. The Calvinists,

Clonmacnoise, on the River Shannon below Athlone, was the greatest monastic site of the early Christian era. Founded by St Ciaran in the 6th century, it was the nearest thing to a proper urban centre in Gaelic Ireland. Later, it was the site of a Norman castle, now in ruins (left). But enough of the original monastic remains have survived (right) to remind us of its glory.

in particular, established themselves within this industrial economy. The sort of dissident Calvinism that erupted briefly in 1798 and might have led to a junction with republicans in the south was now well and truly dead. All of Protestant Ulster, Anglican and Calvinist alike, was now firmly tied to the greater Protestant British state, both by blood and by material interest.

The Great Famine of 1845–1852 was the last great subsistence crisis in Western Europe. Over a million people died; another million fled overseas to escape the hunger and disease. Before the famine, the population of Ireland was over 8 million; by 1861, it was less than 6 million; by 1911, it was below 4.5 million. The Famine was caused by the repeated failure of the potato, the staple crop of the Irish poor. Its effects were intensified by the failure of the British government to give sufficient public funds to relieve the distress. All this happened in the south and west of Ireland while the industrial revolution was making eastern Ulster rich.

Partition

After the Famine, the nationalist demand in most of Ireland focused first on land reform and then on politics. A series of rural agitations, supported by Irish Members of Parliament in London, produced a succession of land reforms in the period 1870–1903 culminating in a scheme whereby the landlords – the successors of the old Ascendancy – sold to the state which in turn sold the land to the tenant farmers, financing the scheme through long-term, low-interest loans.

Political nationalism continued to advance, but more slowly. Home rule was finally achieved in 1914 but suspended because of the outbreak of the Great War. Then, in 1916, republican separatists – for whom home rule was not enough – organised a rebellion in Dublin. It was quickly suppressed by the British but over the next five years the nationalist demands became ever more radical. A guerilla war was fought between Irish nationalists and British from 1919 to 1921. Finally, there was a compromise. Ireland was given independence, but not full republican status. That came eventually in 1949.

But there was a price, and that price was partition. Protestant Ulster stayed within the United Kingdom, where its national allegiance lay. But within Northern Ireland, as the partitioned entity was known, there was a Catholic minority of about 35%, who felt betrayed and cut off from the rest of nationalist Ireland.

Politics in the 20th Century

The Republic of Ireland is now a full member state of the European Union and a country which is secure in its own identity and place in the world. There are, of course, many problems. The country is relatively poor by general European standards; unemployment rates are high; emigration is a constant problem. But by and large, Irish independence has been a success.

Politics in the Republic is confusing for the visitor. The parties are divided less by the normal European criteria of left and right than by the legacy of the Anglo-Irish settlement of 1922. Those who accepted the settlement formed the historic basis of the Fine Gael (Family of Gaels) party. Those who rejected it, thus touching off a short but vicious civil war, later became Fianna Fail (Soldiers of Destiny). Ironically, within ten years the latter had become the largest party, a position they still hold. Both parties are cross-class alliances on the American model, although the more populist Fianna Fail have traditionally had a greater appeal to the working class. Fine Gael draws its main support from the urban bourgeoisie and the larger farmers. The Labour Party is basically a trade union vehicle, although it draws some liberal middle-class support from time to time.

Northern Ireland, unlike the Republic, has been chronically unstable. From 1922 to 1972, it was run as a Protestant fortress in which Catholics were second-class citizens. This discrimination resulted in a Catholic revolt which developed into what are now known as the Troubles. The Irish Republican Army (IRA) attempted to overthrow Northern Ireland by force, claiming descent from the republican and revolutionary tradition of the 1790s. In fact, it is more like a sectarian Catholic militia. Its campaign has failed.

The underlying political problem in Northern Ireland is as intractable as ever.

Is it possible to reconcile two different ethnic groups who want totally opposite things: Ulster Protestants, British by blood and tradition, who want Northern Ireland to remain part of the United Kingdom; and Ulster Catholics, who want the end of partition and the restoration of Irish unity?

Despite this long history of conflict and opposed aspirations, it would be wrong to think of Ireland – and this includes Northern Ireland – as an especially violent place. In most parts of the island, crime rates are low by international standards. Only in the most deprived areas of the larger cities are there chronic problems of drugs, theft, assault and organised crime. Most of the island is slow-moving and relaxed by general European standards and most people are spontaneous, informal and friendly. Even in the worst days of the Troubles, Northern Ireland seldom gave the appearance of a battle zone. To the surprise of visitors, what struck them was its sheer ordinariness.

Perhaps the most significant fact about Ireland in the last thirty years is that it is progressively becoming an urban society.

The movement of population from west to east and from countryside to city has been relentless. In turn, the new generation of Irish people has behaved like most urban people everywhere: they are more cosmopolitan, more style-conscious and less beholden to tradition than their parents. Young Irish people feel themselves to be self-consciously European. One hears less emphasis today on those features of Irish life that are particular to the island and more on those links that connect the island to the outside world.

That is not to say that tradition has been set aside. In North and South alike, it has been transformed and in many cases muted. But in the North it is never far away. Sadly, among the most persistent northern traditions are some that are especially malign. The sectarian hatred and suspicion that occasionally boils over, keeping the two communities apart, shows no signs of abating.

Near Cahersiveen, County Kerry, this ruined
15th-century tower house was once the seat of
the MacCarthy Mor, the local Gaelic chieftain. By
the late medieval period, Gaelic chiefs had long
since learned the techniques of tower house
construction from the Normans.

Double page before:
A general view of the ruins of Clonmacnoise as
the sun sets on the Shannon. In the foreground,
high crosses; in the background, one of the two
surviving round towers and one of the church
buildings.

The ruined abbey of St Fionan Cam in Derrynane
Bay, County Kerry.

Following page:
The pretty village of Kinsale, County Cork,
stands at the mouth of the River Bandon. It is a
popular sailing centre but is most famous for its
outstanding restaurants.

The Provinces

Ireland comprises four provinces: Leinster in the east, Munster in the south, Connacht in the west and Ulster in the north. Let us look at them in that order.

Leinster

Leinster is a province of rolling river valleys and plains. The only major upland areas are the Wicklow Mountains just to the south of Dublin, the Slieve Bloom Mountains in Co. Offaly and the Blackstairs Mountains in Co. Carlow.

The east coast was the traditional invasion route as well as the traditional trade route. Leinster is orientated towards Britain. It is, therefore, the most Anglicised province in Ireland. It has more people of Norman descent than any other and its principal centre of population, Dublin – the national capital – was for centuries the centre of English royal power.

But its importance long precedes the English. The eastern lowlands are rich, fertile and therefore a great source of wealth. To the north-west and south-west of Dublin, there stretches some of the finest pasture land in Europe. Counties Meath and Kildare are famous for thoroughbred horses: the headquarters of Irish racing is at the Curragh in Co. Kildare. Here, the Irish Derby, one of the richest races in the world, is run every summer.

The river valleys of the south-east, where the Norman legacy is strongest, are steeped in history. The provincial city of Kilkenny stands in the heart of this region. Once the centre of the Butler family – their magnificent castle still dominates the place – it is among the most splendidly preserved of Irish urban centres. South of it, along the valley of the Nore, lie the lovely villages of Thomastown and Inistioge.

The Nore joins the Barrow – the second longest river in Ireland – just above New Ross, Co. Wexford. A few miles further downstream, the Barrow is joined by the Suir – the third of these "three sisters" – which drains much of east Munster. The confluence of these three river forms the magnificent Barrow estuary, one of Ireland's great waterways.

At the mouth of the Suir lies the city of Waterford, a Viking foundation now famous for its glassware. Its most famous landmark is Reginald's Tower, a Viking structure which dates from 1003. Further east, the River Slaney enters the sea at Wexford, another town steeped in history. It was the headquarters of the 1798 rebels. Many memorials to that time can be seen around the town and the county. Nowadays, Wexford is most famous for its international opera festival every October, one of the highlights of the Irish social calendar.

Waterways are the key to the province. At Dublin, the Liffey enters the sea. Thirty miles to the north, at the important provincial town of Drogheda, Co. Louth, the Boyne becomes tidal. The Boyne valley, flowing through the richest parts of Co. Meath, has been a centre of civilised life in Ireland since pre-historic times.

Less than ten miles up the Boyne valley, to the west of Drogheda, lie the three great Neolithic burial sites of Newgrange, Knowth and Dowth. Of these, Newgrange is the most famous and the most thoroughly excavated. It is a miracle of construction. The burial chamber in which the dead prince was interred lies at the end of a long passage which is so artfully constructed that the sunlight can penetrate its full distance on one day of the year only: the morning of the winter solstice. After 3,500 years, this astonishing construction is still so sensitively and exquisitely orientated towards the winter sun that on that day alone the sun's ray illuminates the burial chamber. Newgrange is one of the sights of Europe.

Munster

The eastern part of Munster is very similar to Leinster: rich limestone plains and river valleys. Its principal city, Cork, was originally an ancient monastic site and later a Viking settlement. The Normans consolidated its urban status and confirmed its position as the administrative centre of the south.

Cork is the second city of the Republic and a place of very distinctive character. Rising up on both sides from its centre in the valley of the Lee, it is very attractively sited. It is proud of its place as a cultural centre. It has a fine musical tradition and each year hosts one of Europe's best jazz festivals. It also stages an annual film festival. Western Munster is very different. Here, a series of mountainous

The little church near Ladies' View in Killarney's National Park (left).

Croagh Patrick, near Westport in County Mayo, is Ireland's holy mountain. According to the legend, St Patrick once fasted on the summit for forty days and nights. On the last Sunday of July, thousands of pilgrims walk to the summit in memory of this event.

peninsulas jut out into the Atlantic to provide the very finest scenic views in the whole country. Whereas the plains of Munster were largely Norman, the upland areas retained their Gaelic spirit. In parts of the extreme west, on the very margins of the island, Irish is still spoken as a vernacular, although much threatened by the cosmopolitan and anglophone influences of the mass media.

At the centre of the west Munster region, in Co. Kerry, is Killarney, the most famous and fabled beauty spot in Ireland. The town is unremarkable, but all around there is scenery of dramatic grandeur. Two lakes, the majestic Magillycuddy's Reeks – the highest mountains in Ireland – and a succession of magnificent views all contribute to a unique experience. A nineteenth-century visitor called Killarney "heaven's reflection". Few modern visitors will disagree. The county town in Kerry is Tralee, the focus of the Festival of Kerry which takes place every autumn. Based on a competition to find each year's "Rose of Tralee" – the original Rose was the heroine of a popular love song – it is

the most popular, if not perhaps the most sophisticated, festival in Ireland. Equally unsophisticated, but very traditional indeed, is Puck Fair which takes place in Killorglin, Co. Kerry, every August. A three-day harvest festival which has pre-Christian echoes, it is not for the faint-hearted!

No visitor to Ireland should miss Co. Clare, the part of Munster north of the Shannon estuary. Here is the heartland of Irish traditional music, some of the finest coastal scenery including the Cliffs of Moher – the highest cliffs in the country – and the Burren in the north of the county. The Burren is an extraordinary eco-system, created and preserved by the limestone landscape, which is not only unique in appearance but provides a natural habitat for hundreds of flowers and plants that otherwise are hardly found outside Alpine regions, and never this far north.

Munster, like Ireland as a whole, is richest in the east. The west is more rugged, more dramatically beautiful but also poorer. For the quintessential western experience, however, we must turn to the most western province of all.

Connacht

Although Co. Clare is formally in Munster, its geology and geography are of Connacht. Connacht comprises the region west of the river Shannon, north of Clare and south of the line of low hills and lakes that mark the boundary with south-west Ulster. Although parts of the province are east of the river, most of Connacht lies beyond the great river. The Shannon is the longest river in Britain or Ireland; with its tributaries, it drains over a fifth of the entire island. It is a paradise for cruising. It is also a formidable natural barrier and a symbolic boundary. For all Irish people, the expression "west of the Shannon" has a mythical as well as a literal resonance.

Lying between the Shannon and the Atlantic, Connacht consists of inland plains and bogs and coastal mountains dropping onto an Atlantic shoreline in-dented with coves and bays. Land quality is poorer than in the other provinces: this is a land of storm-bent trees, dry-stone walls and high, dramatic cloud formations. Historically, it has retained the smallest Viking and Norman legacy and is often thought of as the most

Gaelic and traditional part of Ireland. Galway is the principal city. Even in medieval times, it had important trading links with Spain and there is a residual Spanish influence to this day: in the sallow skin of some Galway people, in the survival of certain traditional forms of clothing – shawls and cloaks – which have a Spanish appearance and, not least, in the Spanish Arch, one of the city's leading landmarks. It is now a thriving university town and a centre of the arts. It bustles with life and energy.

To get the real flavour of Ireland at play, the visitor should go to the Galway Races, a three-day festival of racing held every August. It is simply great fun. Another distinctive celebration is the Galway Oyster Festival, also an annual event. Just down the road in Clarinbridge, at an inlet of Galway Bay, they have their own oyster festival which is even older than Galway's. Visit both! Oysters and Guinness are among the very finest tastes of Ireland. To the west of Galway city is Connemara; one of Ireland's most distinctive sub-regions. It is dominated by the Twelve Bens, while around the coast lie a succession of

charming ports and villages which are very popular with summer visitors. Lough Corrib, the second-largest lake in Ireland, is one of a series of magnificent fishing lakes that run north of here through the whole province. Parts of South Connemara are still Irish-speaking.

North Connacht brings us to Counties Mayo and Sligo, the latter indelibly linked with the name of the poet W.B. Yeats. The greatest of Irish poets, he spent much of his childhood here and always regarded Sligo as a magical place. He is buried at Drumcliff churchyard, just north of Sligo town. The annual Yeats Summer School recalls his life and work. Indeed, summer schools on every topic under the sun are now a regular feature of Irish life. A full list of subjects, dates and venues is available from the tourist board.

Ulster

This is Ireland's divided province. It is divided politically by the border between the Republic and Northern Ireland: three of its counties, Cavan, Monaghan and Donegal, are in the republic; the remaining six comprise Northern Ireland,

still a part of the United Kingdom. And within Northern Ireland itself, the people are divided by national allegiance. The Protestant majority are mainly the descendants of those Anglo-Scots planters who settled these lands after the defeat of the old Gaelic kingdoms in the early 17th century. The Catholic minority, who wish for reunification with the rest of nationalist Ireland, are principally descended from Gaelic farmers and tenants displaced at that time.

Culturally, Ulster divides in three. East of the River Bann, which itself divides Northern Ireland in two, lie the counties of Antrim and Down, the Protestant heartland. West of the Bann, but still in Northern Ireland, the Catholics are actually in a local majority; this region spills across the border to embrace the magnificent coastal county of Donegal, with scenery as fine as any in the country. Finally, the southern border counties in the Republic – Cavan and Monaghan – are part of the lakeland country that connects both to Leinster to the south as well as to Counties Fermanagh and Tyrone immediately to the north.

Ulster's two cities make an interesting contrast. Belfast is a classic 19th-century industrial city. Derry is a frontier town, complete with its original 17th-century defensive walls still intact. Belfast faces the sea, Britain and the wider world. Derry faces Donegal and the valley of the river Foyle, on which it stands. Both cities have seen great improvements in recent years. The Belfast Festival is the most important cultural event in the life of Northern Ireland, bringing many international performers in all media to the province.

The other urban centre in Ulster that repays a visit is Armagh, the ancient ecclesiastical capital of Ireland. But the most celebrated of all Irish tourist sites lies on the magnificent North Antrim coast. The Giant's Causeway, a series of terraced hexagonal basalt steps reaching into the North Channel near the village of Bushmills – home of the famous whiskey, distilled in the world's oldest working distillery – is a geological survival from the end of the Ice Age.

Ulster is the home of some of Ireland's oldest sagas and legends. Even in pre-Celtic times, it was a fabled land. The most famous of the ancient Irish sagas is the so-called Ulster Cycle. These tales tell of the warriors of Ulster and their heroic deeds. They are fascinating survivals from that pre-Celtic, pre-Christian world which is now almost completely lost to us. The most famous of the tales is the Tain Bo Cuailgne (The Cattle Raid of Cooley) in which the Ulster hero, Cuchulainn, defeats all comers.

Modern Ulster, on the other hand, has been profoundly shaped by the material world. The Protestant settlers of the 17th century created a modernising agricultural economy in what had been the most remote and backward Irish province. Later on, the industrial revolution in Ulster accelerated this process.

Ulster has always been different, often closer to Scotland than to the rest of Ireland in times when the sea passage was easier than land travel. From earliest times, this has been the case. It remains so to this day. The majority Protestant denomination in Ulster is Presbyterian or Calvinist, reflecting a specifically Scottish link. Such links are as old as recorded history. The ancient kingdom of Dalriada comprised north-east Ulster and the Western Isles of Scotland: it reappeared in later history in other forms. Southern Ulster, on the other hand, was safe from invasion until the 16th century behind its natural defences of low hills and lakes. It was terra incognita, a place apart.

The pretty little village of Carnlough lies on the beautiful Antrim coast road. Nearby, the nine Glens of Antrim drop dramatically to the coast.

Dingle, County Kerry, an attractive little fishing
town near the western end of the peninsula
of the same name in County Kerry. It once had
the most westerly railway station in Europe,
although sadly the line is now closed.

Double page before:
Near Ownagarry Bridge, a few miles from
Killorglin in County Kerry.

To the west of Dingle, at the very end of the peninsula, is some of the loveliest scenery in all of Ireland. This little cove is at Ballydavid Head.

Fishing boats moored at the quayside in Dingle
(small picture).

The Iveragh Peninsula is the largest of Kerry's
three peninsulas. Its deeply indented coastline
contains some wonderful beaches, like this one
on Derrynane Bay.

The warm climate of the south-west is ideal for summer flowering shrubs, like these hydrangeas, red-hot pokers and wild fuchsia (above, left and right). Wild flowers at Bull's Head on the southern shore of the Dingle Peninsula (left) and at Dog's Point, near Ardgroom on the Beara Peninsula on the borders of Cork and Kerry (right).

The Cliffs of Moher near Doolin in County Clare.

Double page before:
Looking south across Tralee Bay towards the
mountains of the Dingle Peninsula from the golf
course at Barrow, with a ruined tower house in
the foreground.

This dramatic castle turret stands on the coast of
County Clare near Doolin.

Doorways of Ireland.

The ruins of Hore Abbey, on the lush plains of
Tipperary, near Cashel. It was the last Cistercian
foundation in Ireland prior to the Reformation.

King John's Castle on the banks of the Shannon
in Limerick is one of the very finest Hiberno-
Norman fortifications. It dates from the very
beginning of the thirteenth century (right,
above).
O'Brien's Tower near Liscannor on the Cliffs of
Moher recalls the pre-eminence of the O'Brien
family in County Clare (right, below).

Near Glengarriff, County Cork. This village at the head of an indented harbour on the north shore of Bantry Bay is famous for its lush vegetation (above).

Mizen Head in West Cork is the most southerly point on the Irish mainland (left).

The mouth of the River Blackwater at Youghal, County Cork (above).

The coast of County Cork, near the mouth of the River Bandon at Kinsale (right).

Irish Writers

Ireland has produced four Nobel laureates for literature together with a host of other writers of importance. For a small country, not wealthy or powerful, its literary achievement is by any standard exceptional.

Ironically, the writer considered by many to be the greatest of all never won the Nobel Prize. James Joyce (1882–1941) is probably the most influential novelist of the 20ᵗʰ century in any language. His masterpiece, *Ulysses*, is a dazzling arabesque of Dublin life set on a single day – 16 June 1904 – in which a simple core narrative is presented in an immensely complicated form. The complications can sometimes intimidate the reader but *Ulysses* repays every effort. It is the supreme realistic novel of modern city life. Its method gives the reader a unique insight into the psychology of the characters, in particular that of Leopold Bloom, the advertising salesman around whom most of the action turns. Most of all, *Ulysses* is a comic novel: it is very, very funny. Bloomsday, named for the book's central character, is celebrated annually in Dublin on 16 June. William Butler Yeats (1865–1939) is among the very greatest poets of the modern age. Winner of the Nobel Prize in 1923, his poetry embraced pastoral lyricism, a profound sense of magic and spiritualism, passionate and declamatory involvement in public affairs and, in later life, profound reflection on philosphical themes. His frustrated love for the beautiful Maud Gonne inspired some of his most quoted work. He was also a founder of the Abbey Theatre, the national theatre of Ireland, and was the moving spirit behind the Irish literary revival. Yeats was a force of nature. Every Irish poet since his death has been conscious of his enormous shadow.

George Bernard Shaw (1856–1950) has, by contrast, suffered a fall in his critical fortunes since his death. In life, he was quite simply one of the most famous people in the world. He was a socialist, a vegetarian, a brilliant critic both of theatre and music, the playwright who introduced the realist dramatic methods of Ibsen to a hostile English-speaking world, and a phrase-maker and wit on a heroic scale. He won the Nobel Prize in 1925. But a lot of the causes which he espoused are now discredited and while the plays are still widely performed, they no longer have the power to shock in quite the way that they once did. Always well crafted, they sometimes seem preachy and dated. But perceptions of this sort are largely matters of fashion. There is a core of Shavian achievement which is impervious to changes of fashion, and which will endure.

Samuel Beckett (1906–1989) was an early disciple of Joyce and found sudden fame in the 1950s as one of the leading playwrights of the Theatre of the Absurd. His *Waiting for Godot* is an extended conversation between two tramps who are both waiting for a mysterious, undefined character who never appears. Waiting is all they do, the suggestion being that their condition is emblematic of the emptiness of modern life in general. This play, like his novels, combines a sense of bleakness and futility with a comedy that is often hilarious. Beckett is a complete original, combining laughter and despair as no one else can. He was awarded the Nobel Prize in 1969 and remains one of the 20ᵗʰ century's most distinctive writers.

Seamus Heaney (*1939) is the most celebrated of living Irish writers and the one with

The cemetery on the Rock of Cashel and a ruined castle near Ballyviren Bridge, Co. Cork.

the greatest international reputation. He is part of an exceptional generation of Ulster writers who emerged in the 1960s and '70s. His work is rooted in the rural Ulster of his youth to which he returns over and over again in search of themes and symbols. But from this base, his fluent and image-laden lyrics deal with memory, history, violence and myth. He is a poet who has the most scrupulous regard for language. Heaney is above all a master crafts-man, a careful weaver of words and a poetic technician of the first rank. He is also a distin-guished critic and has held academic positions at Oxford and Harvard. Winner of the Nobel Prize in 1995, he stands at the head of what has been called "Ireland's second literary revival".

The Irish literary tradition is very old, with the earliest fragments of verse surviving from

the 6th century. With the gradual decline of the Irish language, its rich literature became the preserve of a minority. But a succession of brilliant Anglo-Irish writers made a telling con-tribution to English literature. Among the most celebrated were Jonathan Swift (1667–1745), one of the finest satirists in the language; Edmund Burke (1729–1797), a political philosopher often called the "father of modern English conservatism"; and Oscar Wilde (1854–1900), the supreme comic genius of the fin-de-siècle.

Three modern playwrights deserve at-tention. John Millington Synge (1871–1909), established Irish 20th-century drama with plays of mesmeric power and poetic language. Sean O'Casey (1880–1964) introduced a note of gritty urban realism which combined comedy and tragedy. Brian Friel (*1929) has established an international reputation with plays that look anew at the Irish past and its contemporary legacy.

Finally, three living writers. William Trevor (*1928) is the finest modern practitioner of the short story. John Banville (*1945) is a novelist whose work is not confined to Irish themes and is characterised by high intelligence and the most careful use of language. Derek Mahon (*1941) is considered

by many a finer poet than Heaney; his best work is absolutely outstanding.

This brief survey has omitted so many names that it can only give a hint of the rich-ness of the Irish literary tradition. Ireland is a land of words, famous for its talkers as well as its writers. One English critic has written that "if the English hoard words like misers, the Irish spend them like sailors". It is a fertile soil for literature.

Creagh Gardens, near Baltimore, County Cork.

Double page before:
Glendalough, with a view of St Kevin's Kitchen
beyond the stream.

Dunbrody Abbey, on the eastern shore of the
Barrow estuary in south County Wexford, was a
Cistercian foundation dating originally from the
late twelfth century.

48

The round tower at Glendalough is one of the
best preserved in Ireland.

Another view of the round tower at
Glendalough.

A dazzling mixture of heather and gorse on the
coast near Crookhaven, County Cork.

Monuments in stone. Birr Castle (left) is one of the finest and best-preserved castles in Ireland and is still inhabited. Tintern Abbey (right), standing near an inlet of Bannow Bay in County Wexford, was a sister foundation of the great Cistercian abbey of the same name in Wales, from where its first monks came in the thirdteenth century.

Dublin

Ireland's capital is beautifully sited. It stands at the mouth of the river Liffey, embraced by a wide semi-circular bay. At each end of the bay, the hills of Howth and Killiney offer superb views. To the south, less than an hour's drive from the city centre, are the Wicklow Mountains.

Until the 18th century, Dublin was an insignificant city. There was a Viking core, a castle and two cathedrals. Otherwise, there was no building of any distinction. Visitors often compared it unfavourably with English cities and towns.

Then came the glories of Georgian Dublin. The word Georgian is used to cover the period of four kings of England, all called George, who reigned successively from 1714 until 1830. In fact, the first of Dublin's monumental buildings, the Royal Hospital at Kilmainham in the south-west of the city, was built in the 1680s, as a home for old soldiers. It was modelled on Les Invalides in Paris. Its original function has long since been superseded and in recent years it has been restored as Ireland's Museum of Modern Art.

It is to the Georgian age proper that we now turn, for the buildings of that period are the essential Dublin. Let's take a walking tour, starting in the heart of the city at College Green. On one side of the street, curving around the corner into Westmoreland Street, is the Bank of Ireland, formerly the old Parliament House. It was built in the early 1730s, with the curved addition coming in the 1770s. When the old Irish parliament was abolished in 1800, the building was bought by the Bank of Ireland.

On the far side of College Green stands the west front of Trinity College, dating from

1759. The college itself was founded in the 1590s but all its surviving buildings are 18th century or later. The west front is especially fine, but the whole campus is a delight. Classical, Victorian and Modern styles of architecture co-exist in a seemingly effortless harmony. In the Old Library you can see the Book of Kells, the most famous of the ancient Irish manuscripts.

Back at the front of Trinity, turn left and follow the college railings round into Nassau Street. Take the second turn on the right into Kildare Street and half-way up pause outside Leinster House, built in the 1740s as the town house of the Duke of Leinster. Nowadays, it is the home of the post-independence Irish parliament.

Continue to the top of Kildare Street where it joins St Stephen's Green, turn left into

Merrion Row and then left again into Merrion Street. Passing the fine Government Buildings (1911) on your left you come to the back of Leinster House and Merrion Square. Look along the marvellous vista of Merrion Square South and Upper Mount Street which is enclosed at the far end by the little church known in Dublin as the Pepper Canister Church.

This is the heart of Georgian Dublin. Merrion Square, Mount Street, Baggot Street and Fitzwilliam Square are all adjacent. They make a delightful stroll. It is the unity and harmony of these houses, rather than their individual brilliance, that creates the magic.

The two greatest individual buildings of Georgian Dublin are not in this area, however, but on the quays that enclose the Liffey for most of its course through the city. Both were

designed by 18th-century Dublin's greatest architect, James Gandon. The Custom House (1791) is a masterpiece, a miracle of balance and classical symmetry. Further upstream, beyond Capel Street Bridge, lies the Four Courts, the headquarters of the Irish legal system, with its great copper dome dominating this part of the city.

Other buildings of note include the General Post Office (GPO) in O'Connell Street, where the rebels of 1916 had their headquarters; Dublin Castle; and the two cathedrals of St Patrick's and Christ Church, both close to the Castle and to each other, both originally medieval but heavily restored in the 19th century. Finally, no visitor to Dublin should miss the Phoenix Park, the largest city park in Europe. And after a long day's touring, there is no better way to relax than in one of Dublin's fine

pubs with a pint of Guinness, Ireland's delicious national drink.

The Irish soccer team, together with the national drink, inspired this colourful mural on the wall of a pub in Ardgroom, Co. Cork (left).

The eastward view down the River Liffey in central Dublin shows O'Connell Bridge and the green dome of the Custom House in the background. But the whole scene is spoiled by the hideous Liberty Hall, brutally destroying the horizontal harmonies of the Liffey quays.

Two views of the Custom House, completed in 1791. It was the masterpiece of James Gandon, Georgian Dublin's greatest architect. The view from the south side of the river (left) also gives a glimpse of the new Financial Services Centre, a splendid piece of sympathetic modern design. The view looking west (right) also takes in Liberty Hall in the background. The Custom House was burned in 1921 during Ireland's War of Independence. Although subsequently restored, the dome was not rebuilt in the original Portland Stone, but in the cheaper and darker Ardbracken Stone.

Two views of Mayo: the Aasleagh Falls on the
River Erriff in County Mayo (left) and Croagh
Patrick from the shore of Lough Nacorra.

Kylemore Abbey in the heart of Connemara is a nineteenth-century Gothic revival jewel, originally built as a family home by a wealthy Englishman. In 1920, it was sold to the Benedictine nuns who now run it as an exclusive boarding school for girls.

Impressions of an Irish harbour.

The Atlantic spills over the harbour wall at Louisburgh, County Mayo as Croagh Patrick looms in the distance.

The North Antrim coast is one of the great undiscovered secrets of Ireland. Here, near the town of Ballycastle, is White Head which contains the ruins of Kenbane Castle. Kenbane is a corruption of the Gaelic words for "white head". The castle was originally built in 1547.

Double page before:
The great creviced side of Ben Bulben, County Sligo, one of the most dramatic of all Irish mountains. Near here, in the little churchyard at Drumcliff, is buried the great poet W.B. Yeats.

Carnlough, County Antrim.

Samuel Johnson famously said that it was worth
seeing but not worth going to see: the Giant's
Causeway, near Bushmills, County Antrim, is
probably the most celebrated natural feature in
all of Ireland. Comprising over 40,000 polygonal
basalt columns, the legend had it that it was the
work of a mythical giant who was attempting to
build a bridge to Scotland.

A coastal view looking east from the village of
Ballintoy, County Antrim, towards the cliffs of
Fair Head in the background on the right and
Rathlin Island on the left.

A romantic view of the ruined tower house near
Cahersiveen, County Kerry.

Double page before:
The North Antrim coast between the Giant's
Causeway and Fair Head is full of dramatic
indentations and sea stacks.

The end of the rainbow: Whiddy Island in Bantry
Bay, County Cork.

Atlantic

Ocean

Aran Island

Malin Head

Lough
Swilly

Lough
Foyle

★ *Dunluce
Castle*

Coleraine

Errigal Mountain ▲

752

Donegal

Londonderry

Antrim

Rocky Point

Strabane

Londonderry

683
▲

Ballymena

**Northern
Ireland**

Larne

Donegal
Dún na nGall

Omagh

Uls**t**er

Belfast Lough

Belfast ✈

Bangor

Erris Head

Tyrone

Lough
Neagh

Newtownards

North Channel

Sligo
Sligeach

Fermanagh

Portadown

Lisburn

*Strangford
Lough*

Moyne Abbey ★

Mayo

Sligo

Enniskillen

Leitrim

Lower
Lough
Erne

Armagh

Down

Armagh

Newry

Achill Island

C

*Lough
Conn*

Ballina
Béal an Atha

▲ 586

Upper
Lough
Erne

Monaghan

Cavan
An Cabhán

Cavan

Dundalk
Dún Dealgan

852
▲

Castlebar
Caisle in a'Bharraigh

Roscommon

Longford

Louth

852
▲

Westport
Cathair na Mart

o

*Lough
Mask*

Roscommon
Ros Comáin

Longford
Longphort

Abbey ★

Kells
Ceanannas

Newgrange
★

Drogheda
Droichead Átha

▲ 817
Mweelrea

n

n

Tuam
Tuaim

Suck

*Lough
Ree*

Mullingar
An Muileann Cearr

Navan
An Uaimh ★

Boyne

Clifden
An Cloghán

Galway

*Lough
Corrib*

a

c

h

Athlone
Áth Luain

Westmeath

Royal

Canal

Meath

Dublin

Connemara

t

Galway
Gaillimh

★ *Athenry
Castle*

Abbey ★
Clonmacnoise

Tullamore
Tulach Mhór

DUBLIN
✈

Aran Islands

Galway Bay

Shannon

*Lough
Derg*

Grand Canal

Offaly

L e i n s t e r

Kildare
Cill Dara

BAILE ÁTHA CLIATH

Dún Laoghaire

REPUBLIC OF

Clare

Ennis
Inis

Port Laoise

Laois

Glendalough
Round Tower ★

Bray
Bri Chualann

Wicklow

Wicklow
Cill Mhanntáin

Kilkee
Cill Chaoidhe

Nenagh
Aonach Urmhumhan

Carlow
Ceatharlach

**Wicklow
Mountains**
▲ 926

Arklow
An tInbhear Mór

Loop Head

Shannon

Limerick
Luimneach

▲ 694

Tipperary

Carlow

Lugnaquillia Mtn.

IRELAND

Foynes
Faing

Maigue

Golden

Kilkenny
Cill Chainnigh

793 ▲

Wexford

Feale

Limerick

Tipperary
Tiobraid Árann

★ *Rock of
Cashel*

Kilkenny

*Jerpoint
Abbey* ★

Wexford
Loch Garman

Gallarus ★

▲ *Brandon*

Tralee
Tráighli

M u n s t e r

Vale

919

Suir

Clonmel
Cluain Meala

Barrow

Rosslare
Ros Láire

953 *Mountain*

*Slea
Head*

Dingle Bay

Blackwater

Waterford

Waterford
Port Láirge

*Carnsore
Point*

Carrauntoohill
1041 ▲

Killarney
Cill Áirne

Dungarvan
Dún Garbháin

Valencia Island

Kerry

Kenmare
Neidin

Blarney Castle
★

Youghal
Eochaill

St. George's Channel

Lee

Cork
Corcaigh

Caha Mtns.

Bantry
Beanntraighe

Cork

Bandon
*Droichead na
Banndan* ✈

★ *King Charles' Fort*

Bantry Bay

Mizen Head

Celtic Sea

Irish Sea

0   100 km

Glossary

Art and Museums

In Dublin, the National Gallery of Ireland is in Merrion Square and contains an impressive collection of Irish and international painting and sculpture. The Hugh Lane Municipal Gallery of Modern Art in Parnell Square is named for its principal benefactor, who bequeathed it his outstanding collection of Impressionist masterpieces. The Royal Hospital in Kilmainham is the site of the Irish Museum of Modern Art, in which contemporary works in all media are exhibited. The National Museum of Ireland is in Kildare Street, although additional premises have now been secured in Benburb Street. The museum contains the greatest collection of antiquities in Ireland.

No visitor to Dublin should miss the Temple Bar area, just off the south quays between O'Connell Bridge and Capel Street Bridge. It is a hive of galleries, restaurants, arts centres, small theatres and street life. Its most notable centre is the Ark, the only arts centre in Europe wholly dedicated to children. It has indoor and outdoor theatres, exhibition and workshop spaces and lecture rooms all built to the needs of children, with child-sized seating etc.

The Crawford Museum in Cork and the Ulster Museum in Belfast are both worth a visit. The latter is especially good, for in addition to its fine art collection it also has good sections on antiquities – including an excellent exhibit of wreckage salvaged from ships of the Spanish Armada (1588) which went aground on the Ulster coast – and natural history.

Food and Drink

Wonderful brown bread and soda bread. Smoked salmon. The freshest vegetables from the least polluted land in Europe. And most of all, fish, fish, fish. You can eat like a prince in Ireland.

The capital of Irish gastronomy is Co. Cork. The villages of Kinsale and Schull, in particular, are centres of excellence. Near Shanagarry, Ballymaloe House is one of the country's most famous country house restaurants, whose cookery school is run by Darina Allen, Ireland's TV cook extraordinaire.

In Dublin, the Restaurant Patrick Guilbaud is one of the very few restaurants anywhere to have received two Michelin stars. Northern Ireland's best restaurant is Roscoff in Belfast.

But you can eat well almost anywhere. Most pubs serve food, some to a very high standard. Watch out in particular for pubs that have won an award for the quality of their food – they will generally have a sticker on the door or the window announcing the fact. This is part of a national scheme designed to improve the standards of pub catering. It is sponsored by Guinness, speaking of which ...

Guinness is a stout. It is black with a creamy head. It looks good and tastes better and you can drink it with almost anything. With any form of fish it is delicious, with oysters it is ambrosial! Other Irish stouts which are excellent are Beamish and Murphy's, both brewed in Cork. Irish whiskey has long been outshone by Scotch. This is a pity. Irish whiskey is far better than blended Scotch and the very best is on a par with good single malt Scotches. I particularly recommend Black Bush, a very fine drink indeed.

How to Get There

There are international airports in Dublin, Belfast, Cork, Shannon and near Charlestown, Co. Mayo (Horan International). All receive direct flights from Europe and the United States. Aer Lingus, the Irish state airline, is the principal carrier although Ryanair, a private-sector rival, offers very competitive fares, especially from Britain. Lufthansa has daily flights from Frankfurt to Dublin.

Car ferries from Britain cross the Irish Sea to ports at Larne, Dublin, Dun Laoghaire, Rosslare and Cork. The latter two ports also have direct sailings to and from France. The principal British ports of departure are Stranraer, Liverpool, Holyhead and Fishguard. In France, one can embark at Le Havre, Cherbourg or Roscoff.

In the Republic, the rail system radiates from Dublin to serve Wexford, Waterford, Cork, Tralee, Limerick, Galway, Sligo and Belfast. In Northern Ireland, in addition to local services, there is a main line from Belfast to Derry.

The road system is best in Northern Ireland but the Republic is catching up. Some main roads are excellent but there is relatively little motorway and some stretches of main road are still very narrow. Off the beaten track, however, Ireland still offers relatively empty roads and old-fashioned motoring.

Shopping

For clothes, Ireland produces high fashion items in tweed, woollens, linen and lace. They are found almost anywhere in the country, from the biggest department stores to the smallest boutiques around the coast. Craft shops also abound, specialising in glassware, pottery and silver, much of it quite exquisitely worked and often very reasonably priced. Irish traditional music is hugely popular around the world: music shops have a wide selection of artists of all types on CD and tape. Also, don't forget smoked salmon! It's delicious, and you can buy it in Ireland for a fraction of what it will cost you at home.

And don't forget: the Irish government operates a scheme that allows you to reclaim any VAT (value added tax) charged on gifts bought while visiting the country. Citizens of the European Union can get a refund up to a specific amount – it can change annually, so enquire in the shops when making your purchase. Visitors from outside the EU can reclaim all VAT. The money can be claimed back at your port or airport of departure.

Sport

Ireland is celebrated for its horses and there are racecourses all over the country with regular meetings. The most famous is the Irish Derby meeting at the Curragh every summer. Other venues are Punchestown, Co. Kildare and Fairyhouse, Co. Meath, both of them dedicated to National Hunt racing (hurdling and steeplechasing). The Irish Grand National meeting takes place at Fairyhouse every Easter Monday. At Laytown, Co. Meath, there is racing on the beach every August – watch the newspapers for the exact date – the only official race meeting to take place on the sands in Britain or Ireland.

The annual Dublin Horse Show takes place at the showgrounds of the Royal Dublin Society every August. Other major horse shows are held in Galway and at Millstreet, Co. Cork. The Irish national sports are Gaelic football and hurling. Football is rather like a mixture of rugby, soccer and Australian Rules but is played with a round ball. It is an exciting but occasionally scrappy game. Hurling, on the other hand, is simply one of those experiences that no one should miss. The world's fastest field sport, it is a dazzling exhibition of skill, courage and style. Played with a stick about the size of a hockey stick but with a much thicker boss which enables the players to lift the ball before striking it, hurling is the quintessential Irish sport. There is only one problem: blink and you'll miss something.

There are some magnificent golf courses all over Ireland, including over ten championship courses. Fishing of all sort is available in abundance, whether game, coarse or sea angling. Finally, there is no finer recreation available in Ireland than hill-walking. The country is full of wonderful hills, which offer walks ranging from the simplest to the most demanding. But be warned! Do not venture on the high mountains alone or without making thorough preparations. There are people killed on the Irish mountains each year.

Tourist Information

Fuller information about all the foregoing is available from tourist offices.

In the Republic, the headquarters of Bord Failte Eireann (the Irish Tourist Board) is at Baggot Street Bridge, Dublin 2.
Tel 01-6765871/01-6616500.
Fax 01-6764764.

The country is divided into the following tourist regions:
Dublin (Dublin city and county)
Dublin Tourism, 1 Clarinda Park North,
Dun Laoghaire, Co. Dublin.
Tel 01-2808571. Fax 01-2802641.

South East (Counties Carlow, Kilkenny,
South Tipperary, Waterford, Wexford)
South East Tourism, 41 The Quay, Waterford.
Tel 051-75823. Fax 051-77388.

South West (Counties Cork, South Kerry)
Cork/Kerry Tourism, Grand Parade, Cork.
Tel 021-273251. Fax 021-273504.

Shannon (Counties Clare, Limerick,
North Kerry, North Tipperary, South Offaly)
Shannon Development Centre, Shannon,
Co. Clare.
Tel 061-361555. Fax 061-361903.

West (Counties Galway, Mayo, Roscommon)
Ireland West Tourism, Aras Failte, Eyre Square,
Galway.
Tel 091-63081. Fax 091-65201.

North West (Counties Cavan, Donegal,
Leitrim, Monaghan, Sligo)
North West Tourism, Aras Reddan,
Temple Street, Sligo.
Tel 071-61201. Fax 071-60360.

East Midlands (Counties Kildare, Laois,
Longford, Louth, Meath, North Offaly,
Westmeath, Wicklow)
Midlands East Tourism, Dublin Road,
Mullingar, Co. Westmeath.
Tel 044-48761. Fax 044-40413.

In Northern Ireland, visitors should contact:
Northern Ireland Tourist Board, 59 North
Street, Belfast BT1 1ND
Tel (01232) 231221 Fax (01232) 240960.

In Germany, the relevant address is:
Irische Fremdenverkehrszentrale, Untermain-
anlage 7, 60239 Frankfurt am Main.
Tel 069-236492. Fax 069-234626.

The Authors

Richard Killeen was born in Dublin in 1953.
He lived in London, Paris and New York before
returning to his native city. He is the author of
the best-selling *Short History of Ireland* and of
The Easter Rising, an illustrated account of the
insurrection of 1916 that changed the face of
modern Ireland.

Marc Berger was born in 1948 in Saar-
brücken and first studied graphic design. After
further studies, he has worked as a
professional photographer since 1982. He
lived abroad for many years and since then has
concentrated mainly on nature and travel
photography. He has published many books in
this field which have appeared world-wide.

Select Bibliography

Bardon, Jonathan, *A History of Ulster*,
Belfast: Blackstaff Press 1992

Boylan, Henry, gen. ed., *A Dictionary of Irish
Biography*, 2nd ed., Dublin: Gill & Macmillan
1988

Brown, Terence, *Ireland: a social and cultural
history*, London: Fontana 1981

Foster, Roy, *Modern Ireland 1600–1972*,
London: Allen Lane/Penguin 1988

Heaney, Seamus, *New Selected Poems
1966–1987*, London: Faber & Faber 1990

Hickey, D. J. and J. E. Doherty, *A Dictionary of
Irish History since 1800*, Dublin: Gill & Macmillan 1980

Kennelly, Brendan, ed., *The Penguin Book of
Irish Verse*, London: Penguin 1970

Killeen, Richard, *A Short History of Ireland*,
Dublin: Gill & Macmillan 1994 (three-language
edition: English, Frensh, German)

Lee, Joseph, *Ireland 1912–1985: politics and
society*, Cambridge: Cambridge University
Press 1989

Mc Redmond, Louis, gen. ed., *Modern Irish
Lives: dictionary of 20th-century Irish
biography*, Dublin: Gill & Macmillan 1996

Moody, Theo and F. X. Martin, eds, *The
Course of Irish History*, Cork: Mercier Press
1967

Welch, Robert, ed., *The Oxford Companion to
Irish Literature*, Oxford: Oxford University Press
1996

Yeats, W. B., *Collected Poems*, London:
Macmillan 1950

MOTHERCARE

PREGNANCY
WEEK BY WEEK

Nina Grunfeld

Conran Octopus

Contents

Introduction **4**

Weeks 1–13

The first trimester

Pregnancy tests **6**
Now you're pregnant **7**

Ovulation and fertilization **8**
Pregnancy dangers **9**

Conception **10**
Healthy eating **11**

You and your developing
baby **12** Your due date **13**

You and your developing
baby **14** Star signs **15**

You and your developing
baby **16** Your relationship **17**

You and your developing
baby **18** Mixed emotions **19**

You and your developing
baby **20** Looking good **21**

You and your developing
baby **22** Antenatal care **23**

You and your developing
baby **24** Working in
pregnancy **25**

You and your developing
baby **26**
Common problems 1 **27**

You and your developing
baby **28**
Common problems 2 **29**

You and your developing
baby **30** Homoeopathy and
herbs **31**

To my mother

Weeks 14–27

The second trimester

You and your developing baby **32**　Other children **33**

You and your developing baby **34**　Holidays **35**

You and your developing baby **36**　Ultrasound scan **37**

You and your developing baby **38**　Amniocentesis **39**

You and your developing baby **40**　Pregnancy wardrobe **41**

You and your developing baby **42**　Vitamins and minerals **43**

You and your developing baby **44**　Height of fundus **45**

You and your developing baby **46**　Keeping fit 1 **47**

You and your developing baby **48**　Keeping fit 2 **49**

You and your developing baby **50**　The father's role **51**

You and your developing baby **52**　Problems of later pregnancy **53**

You and your developing baby **54**　Weight gain in pregnancy **55**

You and your developing baby **56**　Preparing for baby **57**

You and your developing baby **58** Shopping for equipment 1 **59**

Weeks 28–40

The third trimester

You and your developing baby **60**　Shopping for equipment 2 **61**

You and your developing baby **62**　Learning relaxation **63**

You and your developing baby **64**　Thinking about feeding **65**

You and your developing baby **66**　Good posture **67**

You and your developing baby **68**　Getting ready **69**

You and your developing baby **70**　Shopping for layette **71**

You and your developing baby **72**　Breathing for labour **73**

You and your developing baby **74**　Pain relief **75**

You and your developing baby **76**　Packing your case **77**

Get ready now **78**　Onset of labour **79**

You and your developing baby **80**　Fathers in labour **81**

You and your developing baby **82**　Positions during labour **83**

You and your developing baby **84**　The birth **85**

The postnatal ward **86**

Understanding your hospital notes **88**

Glossary **90**

Useful addresses **93**

Index **94**

Acknowledgments **95**

Project editor
Jane O'Shea

Project art editor
Ann Burnham

Editor
Carole McGlynn

Project assistant
Debora Robertson

Production
Louise Barratt

Picture research
Nadine Bazar

First published in 1988 by
Conran Octopus Limited
37 Shelton Street
London WC2H 9HN

Reprinted 1989 (twice),
1990 (twice), 1991, 1992 (twice), 1993

ISBN 1 85029 146 2
Typeset by Tradespools Limited
Printed in China

Introduction

This book is a week-by-week guide to what is happening to you and your baby throughout your pregnancy.

On the left-hand pages, 'You and Your Developing Baby' describes the physical and emotional changes you experience and the detailed development of your baby. You will find this a useful guideline although, of course, every woman – and every pregnancy – is different so you may feel that what appears under 'You' in Week 7, for example, fits your Week 9 better. In the same way, the weights given for the baby – particularly in the later weeks – can only be an average guide.

You might like to use the diary space on the left-hand pages to write down important appointments and keep a note of your feelings; this will make an interesting record of your pregnancy for later on. We have given important reminders in the relevant weeks under 'Don't forget': for example, your first antenatal visit, making a dental appointment or noting down when you first feel your baby kick.

The right-hand pages for each week feature particular aspects of pregnancy in some detail, from the first doctor's visit to shopping for the layette and baby equipment, as well as advice to expectant fathers and how to prepare yourselves for the birth itself. Some of these features, for example the amniocentesis test and ultrasound scan, are particularly relevant to a certain week while others may vary and many are relevant throughout your pregnancy. Cross-references are included wherever necessary to help you find all the information you want and there is also a full index at the back of the book.

Since medically your pregnancy is dated from the first day of your last period, and not from the time of conception, you may not know you are expecting a baby until you are at least 'five weeks pregnant' – which is actually about two to three weeks after conception, and around the time of your first missed period.

The first few weeks of this book will, in effect, have already happened! You will find them interesting to read before you start following the weeks of the guide. The weeks of your pregnancy may not run from Monday to Sunday as in this book. If, for example, the first day of your last period was a Wednesday, your pregnancy weeks will run from Wednesday to Tuesday. Use the week closest to your own timing.

Each week, fill in the Month and Dates at the top of the page for that particular week – for example, November 24th–30th – so that you can use the diary space for specific appointments.

Throughout the diary your baby is referred to as 'he', not because of any bias but just to differentiate you, the mother, from your baby. The term 'partner' has been chosen to cover the expectant father, no matter what his status.

During pregnancy you will come across lots of new words and terms, especially medical ones. There is a short glossary of the more important of these at the back of the book. Never allow yourself to be confused by these – always ask the doctor or midwife what they mean if you do not understand the terms they are using.

There is also a list of useful addresses at the end of the book. Refer to the groups or associations if you would like more information about any particular topic. For example, if you are expecting twins you may like to know more than can be covered in this book and would find it helpful to contact the Twins Clubs Association.

The forty weeks of pregnancy are conventionally divided into three terms, known medically as 'trimesters'. Many women find that, physically and emotionally, their pregnancy falls into three parts too. Forty weeks can seem a long time and you may find it helpful to have it broken down in some way. We have used coloured bands to differentiate these three terms throughout the book and to help you relate the forty weeks to the actual months of your pregnancy.

A note about the author
When she was about fifteen weeks pregnant, Nina Grunfeld decided to write a book about what happens to mothers and their babies, week by week, during pregnancy. She was by then feeling well, happy and excited about her baby and wanted to convey the emotional ups and downs, the pleasures and concerns of pregnancy.

In Week 40 this book was finished and her first child, Michael, was born.

Nina Grunfeld is 34 years old, married and lives in London. This is her sixth book.

Week 1

Month: Dates:

MON

TUES

WED

THURS

FRI

SAT

SUN

Notes

■ PREGNANCY TESTS

The first, and most reliable, sign of your pregnancy will be a missed period. A less reliable sign will be that you just 'feel pregnant'. To test whether or not you are pregnant, you can buy a home testing kit from your chemist or you can have a pregnancy test done at your doctor's, your family planning clinic or even at some chemists — look for a sign in the window.

The most common pregnancy tests work by detecting a particular hormone in your urine. There is a more concentrated amount of this pregnancy hormone in the first urine you pass in the day, so you need to collect an early-morning sample in a clean, soap-free container. This hormone will show up about four weeks after conception, that is two weeks after the first day of your missed period. If you can't wait, a blood test can tell if you are pregnant before you have missed a period.

Follow the instructions with a kit very carefully. Positive results from a urine test are 99 per cent reliable. If your test is negative then it could be that there isn't yet enough pregnancy hormone to show up in a test. If your period doesn't start, have another test in a week's time.

This is one of several kinds of home testing kit. They all vary slightly so follow the pack instructions.

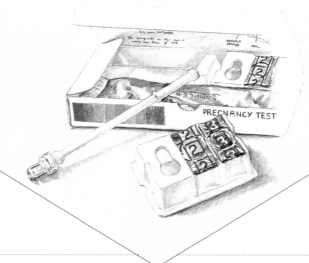

Now you're pregnant

Congratulations on your pregnancy!

You may be one of the lucky ones who find the next forty or so weeks just fly by. Or you may feel pregnancy is a long process during which your body takes over your life. Every woman is different – and every pregnancy is too. Your feelings about pregnancy and parenthood will no doubt change constantly during the course of your pregnancy. Having a baby is rather like going on a blind date – but the build-up is forty weeks and the consequences life-long!

The first fourteen weeks of your pregnancy may well be the hardest, so if you are feeling below par in the initial stages, take heart that things will improve. During early pregnancy, despite the excitement of expecting a baby, you may well feel exhausted and possibly sick. Even if you've been trying to get pregnant for a long time, the reality may make you scared; pregnancy in any case tends to make you over-emotional. You may also worry about the possibility of miscarriage and about whether your baby will be all right. All these fears are perfectly normal and should be discussed with your partner and, if you wish, with your doctor or midwife.

On a practical level you may wonder if you have the money, time or space for a child. You can insure now against twins if you think there's a likelihood of you having them, but even one baby is an expense you may worry about. It might be a good idea to start putting aside some money now, especially if you will be giving up work, and think about economies you can make in your living expenses.

For many women, the middle term of pregnancy is the most exhilarating time of their lives. Make the most of it: if you don't want to do certain things you have the perfect excuse for simply taking it easy. Alternatively, you may find you have enough energy for two during those weeks.

As you get more noticeably pregnant, friends will be full of advice. Listen to it all, but decide how much is relevant to you. Everyone is different and these forty weeks are a time for finding out about yourself.

You may well become inward-looking during pregnancy. This is a good thing. Use the opportunity to rest, relax and get to know yourself. It will be the last time you have on your own for quite a while.

During pregnancy you may feel very romantic and should enjoy these feelings. Your partner no doubt will appreciate all the attention and affection and it may be some time after your baby is born before you feel so sensual again.

Towards the end of your pregnancy it is perfectly natural to feel impatient for it to be over, especially if you feel heavy, unattractive and uncomfortable. You may be filled with conflicting emotions: on the one hand anxious about having the child and giving birth, and yet on the other hand feeling that by now you can't wait to hold your baby. These emotions are perfectly understandable: a new member of your family is about to arrive and you are bound to feel a mixture of excitement together with a reasonable degree of nervousness.

This diary is intended to keep you company during your pregnancy. Use it to write your appointments in, scribble down your feelings, draw pictures of yourself and your bump, or write lists of babies' names. Most of all, try to enjoy your pregnancy. There's nothing left to say but 'Good luck'.

Week 2

Month: _____   Dates: _____

MON

TUES

WED

THURS

FRI

SAT

SUN

Notes

OVULATION AND FERTILIZATION

Ovulation happens each month. It is when a ripe egg, or ovum – a single cell just 0.13mm (0.005in) large – is released from one of your ovaries and travels along your Fallopian tube. At the same time the lining of your womb becomes engorged with blood ready to receive and nourish an embryo and the mucus in your cervix becomes thinner so that sperm can swim through it more easily.

Most women ovulate about fourteen days before a period, whatever the length of their menstrual cycle. If you have an average twenty-eight day cycle, you will have ovulated on about the last day of this week – fourteen days from the first day of your last period.

An egg lives for about twenty-four hours after being released from the ovary, so if you are going to conceive, the egg has to be fertilized within these twenty-four hours. For you to be pregnant, you will have had sexual intercourse shortly before or after you ovulated and your ripe egg will have been fertilized by your partner's sperm. Except in the case of twins, only one sperm will pierce the outer coat of your egg and fertilize it. Instantly the egg loses its attraction, hardens its outer shell and all the other sperm drop off.

Most of the 400 million sperm ejaculated into your vagina (1) leak out, but some swim up through your cervix, into your uterus (2) and then into your Fallopian tube (3) The sperm are attracted to the ovum (4) and stick to its surface.

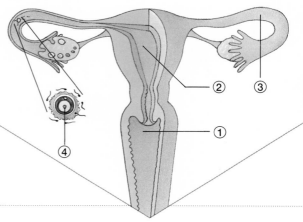

Pregnancy dangers

Once you know you are pregnant, it's time to become more aware of your body and learn to trust your intuition. You must consciously avoid all risks to your unborn child, which means coming to terms with the danger inherent in smoking, drinking and taking drugs. Their possible harmful effects are greatest during the first trimester of pregnancy, when the baby's organs are forming.

Smoking

It is extremely important that you stop smoking as soon as you know you are pregnant. Ask your partner to stop smoking too, to help you give up. Some women who smoke find that they develop a dislike of cigarettes early on in pregnancy; this may even be one of the first ways they know they are pregnant. If you find it impossible to stop smoking completely, at least cut right down.

Smoking during pregnancy increases the risk of early miscarriage and the chances of possible complications at birth – or of a stillborn baby. It has been proved that women who smoke ten or more cigarettes a day during pregnancy have smaller babies. Their children are also at greater risk of having a lower intellect or of being born with mental or physical abnormalities.

Alcohol

It is sensible to cut out alcohol completely, especially for the first three months of pregnancy. If you are planning to become pregnant, it is wise to cut down or stop drinking alcohol. Research shows that drinking alcohol, even in moderation, increases the risk of miscarriage or of a low-birthweight baby. It may also make physical abnormalities, heart defects or some degree of mental retardation more likely.

It obviously helps if you 'go off' alcohol anyway during pregnancy, but even if you don't, cut out spirits completely, and restrict alcohol to the odd glass of wine or beer.

Drugs

Don't take any drugs without consulting your doctor during pregnancy. Many drugs can cross the placenta and cause severe abnormalities in the fetus; even aspirin and sleeping tablets can be harmful, and there are very few antibiotics that can be safely taken during the first three months of pregnancy. A few drugs do not cross the placenta and doctors are careful to prescribe only those known to be safe if you require treatment.

If you suffer from any illness or disorder for which you normally take drugs, tell your doctor if you are planning to become pregnant or immediately you suspect you may be pregnant – he or she may wish to change your course of treatment.

X-rays

Avoid X-rays if possible. If you do need to be X-rayed, it is important to stress that you are pregnant. A chest X-ray would be possible, for example, provided a lead apron was put over your stomach to prevent the rays reaching the baby.

German measles (rubella)

If you get German measles during the first three months of pregnancy your baby may be malformed, deaf, blind or born with heart disease. Rubella can also be the cause of miscarriage or stillbirth. Check whether you have been immunized against it, and keep well away from anyone who has German measles. Tell your doctor at once if you do come into contact with the disease.

How to stop smoking

- ☐ Think of your unborn baby, not just yourself.
- ☐ Tell everyone you are going to stop.
- ☐ Stop today – but keep a packet on you so you know you *could* start again.
- ☐ Put the money you would have spent on cigarettes in a glass jar so you can see how quickly it adds up.
- ☐ Change any habits related to cigarette smoking. Drink orange juice instead of tea or coffee (it's better for baby too).
- ☐ Avoid places where people are smoking.
- ☐ Keep your hands busy – start sewing or knitting baby clothes!
- ☐ If you become tense, breathe deeply and relax (see Week 29).
- ☐ Don't worry about not smoking forever, just worry about not smoking today.

Week 3

Month: Dates:

MON

TUES

WED

THURS

FRI

SAT

SUN

Notes

■ CONCEPTION

During the two weeks after fertilization, the cell that will become your baby multiplies quickly from a single-cell egg into over one hundred cells which will travel along your Fallopian tube until they reach your uterus.

Approximately thirty hours after fertilization, the fertilized cell divides into two identical cells. Roughly ten hours later these two cells divide again, making four cells in all. Within three days, the egg has divided into a total of sixteen cells, which get smaller and smaller with each division. At the same time, the cells are travelling along your Fallopian tube towards your uterus. By about the fourth day after fertilization, the egg, now a round, solid mass of over a hundred cells (and still growing), enters your uterus. It is now called a blastocyst and looks like a tiny blackberry. The blastocyst is formed of two layers: the outer one eventually becomes your placenta and the inner one, your embryo.

During the next few days the blastocyst floats free in the cavity of the uterus and is nurtured by 'milk' secreted from the glands in the uterus lining. By the end of Week 3 the blastocyst will begin to attach itself firmly to your specially thickened womb lining, a process known as implantation. When this has happened, conception is said to have taken place.

Implantation usually takes place in the upper part of the uterus on either the left or right side, depending on which ovary ovulated.

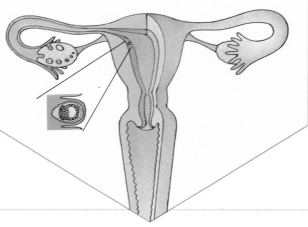

Healthy eating

During pregnancy remember that you are having to provide nutrition not only for yourself but also for your developing baby. This doesn't mean you should go overboard on quantity but that you should eat a good, varied, high-protein diet rich in vitamins and minerals – so start now. Eat fresh food whenever you can and try to cut out sweets, fizzy drinks, cakes, tinned fruit, packet desserts and soups, and chocolate.

Below is a suggested meal plan which you could easily follow during pregnancy. It contains 1500 calories a day. (Your daily intake may well be more or less than this. Be guided by your own appetite and weight gain.) If you are hungry between meals eat raw vegetables or fresh fruit. If you follow a strict diet (vegetarian, vegan or macrobiotic), discuss this with your doctor: you may need to supplement it with extra minerals or vitamins (see Week 19). If you start feeling sick, follow the advice given in Week 7 and revert to this diet once the sickness is over.

What you need in your diet
Protein Pregnant women need at least 75g (3oz) of protein a day, especially if ill or tired. Eat two portions of meat or alternative (see Daily Allowances, right).
Carbohydrates These provide energy, but can make you fat. If you are overweight, eat wholemeal bread and avoid foods containing sugar, alcohol, white flour and rice.

Fibre Fibre (or roughage) will help prevent constipation. Foods with high fibre content are peas and beans; wholemeal bread and cereals; potatoes (especially their skins); fruit, vegetables and nuts.
Fats Cut down on fats. Trim fat off meat; don't fry food or drown it in rich sauces; eat low-fat yoghurt and semi-skimmed milk.
Milk and dairy products Dairy products contain calcium which is important for your baby's development. The diet below will be sufficient for most women during pregnancy, but if you need building up you will need more dairy products.
Vitamins and minerals (see Week 19)

See Week 7 for advice on Morning Sickness

See Week 19 for Vitamins and Minerals

Daily allowances
Milk: 0.4 litre (⅔ pint) semi-skimmed milk; low-fat cheese: 25g (1oz); low-fat yoghurt: 25g (1oz); butter/margarine: 14g (½oz); low-fat spread: 25g (1oz).
Average portion of meat and alternatives
Meat: 75g (3oz); white fish: 100g (4oz); oily fish: 75g (3oz); cottage cheese: 100g (4oz); low-fat cheese: 75g (3oz); 2 eggs; cooked lentils or beans: 150g (6oz).
Average portion of bread and alternatives
Wholemeal bread (1 slice); 1 potato; 1 tablespoon cooked rice or pasta; 1 tablespoon yam, sweet potato, plantain; 1 carton plain yoghurt; 1 extra serving fruit; 3 tablespoons wholegrain cereal; 2 wholemeal crispbreads.

Breakfast
Tomato juice or ½ fresh grapefruit
6 tablespoons wholegrain cereal or 2 slices wholemeal bread and butter from daily allowance (see above)
1 egg or small slice lean grilled bacon or fish
Milk from daily allowance
Mid-morning
Tea, coffee or low-calorie drink
1 fresh fruit or fruit juice

Lunch
Clear soup or tomato juice
Average portion of meat or alternative
2 slices wholemeal bread or alternative (see above)
Large serving of vegetables or salad
1 fruit (as for mid-morning)
Afternoon
Tea, coffee or low-calorie drink
1 fruit (as for mid-morning)

Evening meal
Average portion of meat or alternative (see above)
2 slices wholemeal bread or alternative
Large serving of vegetables or salad
1 fruit (as for mid-morning)
1 low-fat yoghurt or 25g (1oz) low-fat cheese
Bedtime
Tea, coffee or low-calorie drink

Week 4

Month: Dates:

MON

TUES

WED

THURS

FRI

SAT

SUN

Notes

You This is the week of your first missed period. You may be aware of some slight body changes.

Baby At the beginning of Week 4 your pregnancy is just a mass of cells embedded in the lining of your uterus, nourished by the blood vessels there. During Week 4 the cells multiply rapidly and group together to make different structures. The outer layer of cells surrounding the embryo reaches out like roots sending projections into the lining of your uterus. Those which penetrate deepest form the basis of the placenta.

At the same time the inner cells of the embryo form themselves into two, then three layers, each of which will grow to be different parts of your baby's body.

Other cells are developing into the amniotic sac. By the end of the week the embryo is completely embedded in the womb and is just visible to the naked eye.

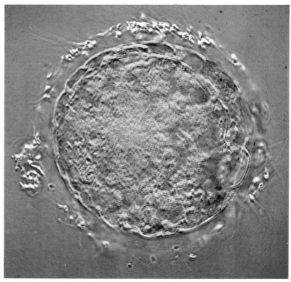

This mass of cells is an early stage of embryonic development. The surrounding pink ring is the debris of sperm that failed to penetrate the ovum.

Your due date

Medically your pregnancy is dated from the first day of your last period, and not from the time of conception. So, what is called 'four weeks pregnant' is actually about two weeks after conception. Worked out like this, the average pregnancy lasts for forty weeks – the length of this diary. Use the chart below to work out the date your baby is due.

If your normal cycle is less than twenty-eight days, your EDD will be a few days earlier than shown, since you ovulate earlier in a short menstrual cycle; conversely, in a cycle regularly longer than twenty-eight days you ovulate later and your EDD will be a few days after the one shown in the chart.

Remember that this is just a rough guide – babies have a habit of arriving either early or late, hardly ever on time. Some people find it a good idea to give friends an EDD about two weeks later than the actual one as it can be quite frustrating at the end of your pregnancy being constantly asked if the baby has arrived yet.

The trimesters

Pregnancy is divided into three trimesters (literally, thirds of pregnancy). The first is the first thirteen weeks, the second lasts from Week 14 to Week 27 and the third is from Week 28 until delivery.

The trimesters are a way of dividing up the forty weeks of pregnancy convenient to the medical profession, but you too will probably find that you naturally think of your pregnancy in three stages of roughly the same duration.

During the first trimester the fetus grows rapidly and all the different parts of the baby are formed. This is the period of greatest risk, both of miscarriage and of drugs causing congenital abnormalities. During the second and third trimesters the baby increases in size and his organs mature sufficiently for him to survive outside the womb. Many women feel at their best during the middle, or second trimester of their pregnancy.

See Week 7 for Morning Sickness

First signs

Morning sickness This is a misnomer. Many women feel sick all day or just in the evenings. Some women only *feel* sick, many actually are.

Tender breasts You may have already noticed your breasts becoming bigger and more sensitive as they can do before your period. They may also tingle slightly.

Exhaustion You may feel faint or dizzy or simply exhausted: try and rest.

Food and taste Some women experience a metallic taste in their mouth which affects their sense of taste. Others just go off certain foods, commonly tea, coffee, alcohol, fatty and fried foods and fish. You may also get cravings for other foods.

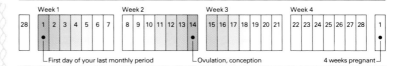

Week 1: 28 | 1 2 3 4 5 6 7 — First day of your last monthly period
Week 2: 8 9 10 11 12 13 14 — Ovulation, conception
Week 3: 15 16 17 18 19 20 21
Week 4: 22 23 24 25 26 27 28 | 1 — 4 weeks pregnant

Month	Figures	Month
JANUARY	1 2 3 4 5 6 7 8 9 10 11 12 13 14 15 16 17 18 19 20 21 22 23 24 25 26 27 28 29 30 31	JANUARY
OCTOBER	8 9 10 11 12 13 14 15 16 17 18 19 20 21 22 23 24 25 26 27 28 29 30 31 1 2 3 4 5 6 7	**NOVEMBER**
FEBRUARY	1 2 3 4 5 6 7 8 9 10 11 12 13 14 15 16 17 18 19 20 21 22 23 24 25 26 27 28	FEBRUARY
NOVEMBER	8 9 10 11 12 13 14 15 16 17 18 19 20 21 22 23 24 25 26 27 28 29 30 1 2 3 4 5	**DECEMBER**
MARCH	1 2 3 4 5 6 7 8 9 10 11 12 13 14 15 16 17 18 19 20 21 22 23 24 25 26 27 28 29 30 31	MARCH
DECEMBER	6 7 8 9 10 11 12 13 14 15 16 17 18 19 20 21 22 23 24 25 26 27 28 29 30 31 1 2 3 4 5	**JANUARY**
APRIL	1 2 3 4 5 6 7 8 9 10 11 12 13 14 15 16 17 18 19 20 21 22 23 24 25 26 27 28 29 30	APRIL
JANUARY	6 7 8 9 10 11 12 13 14 15 16 17 18 19 20 21 22 23 24 25 26 27 28 29 30 31 1 2 3 4 5	**FEBRUARY**
MAY	1 2 3 4 5 6 7 8 9 10 11 12 13 14 15 16 17 18 19 20 21 22 23 24 25 26 27 28 29 30 31	MAY
FEBRUARY	5 6 7 8 9 10 11 12 13 14 15 16 17 18 19 20 21 22 23 24 25 26 27 28 1 2 3 4 5 6 7	**MARCH**
JUNE	1 2 3 4 5 6 7 8 9 10 11 12 13 14 15 16 17 18 19 20 21 22 23 24 25 26 27 28 29 30	JUNE
MARCH	8 9 10 11 12 13 14 15 16 17 18 19 20 21 22 23 24 25 26 27 28 29 30 31 1 2 3 4 5 6	**APRIL**
JULY	1 2 3 4 5 6 7 8 9 10 11 12 13 14 15 16 17 18 19 20 21 22 23 24 25 26 27 28 29 30 31	JULY
APRIL	7 8 9 10 11 12 13 14 15 16 17 18 19 20 21 22 23 24 25 26 27 28 29 30 1 2 3 4 5 6 7	**MAY**
AUGUST	1 2 3 4 5 6 7 8 9 10 11 12 13 14 15 16 17 18 19 20 21 22 23 24 25 26 27 28 29 30 31	AUGUST
MAY	8 9 10 11 12 13 14 15 16 17 18 19 20 21 22 23 24 25 26 27 28 29 30 31 1 2 3 4 5 6 7	**JUNE**
SEPTEMBER	1 2 3 4 5 6 7 8 9 10 11 12 13 14 15 16 17 18 19 20 21 22 23 24 25 26 27 28 29 30	SEPTEMBER
JUNE	8 9 10 11 12 13 14 15 16 17 18 19 20 21 22 23 24 25 26 27 28 29 30 1 2 3 4 5 6 7	**JULY**
OCTOBER	1 2 3 4 5 6 7 8 9 10 11 12 13 14 15 16 17 18 19 20 21 22 23 24 25 26 27 28 29 30 31	OCTOBER
JULY	8 9 10 11 12 13 14 15 16 17 18 19 20 21 22 23 24 25 26 27 28 29 30 31 1 2 3 4 5 6	**AUGUST**
NOVEMBER	1 2 3 4 5 6 7 8 9 10 11 12 13 14 15 16 17 18 19 20 21 22 23 24 25 26 27 28 29 30	NOVEMBER
AUGUST	8 9 10 11 12 13 14 15 16 17 18 19 20 21 22 23 24 25 26 27 28 29 30 31 1 2 3 4 5	**SEPTEMBER**
DECEMBER	1 2 3 4 5 6 7 8 9 10 11 12 13 14 15 16 17 18 19 20 21 22 23 24 25 26 27 28 29 30 31	DECEMBER
SEPTEMBER	7 8 9 10 11 12 13 14 15 16 17 18 19 20 21 22 23 24 25 26 27 28 29 30 1 2 3 4 5 6 7	**OCTOBER**

Menstrual calendar (top)
This shows a regular 28-day cycle. Your pregnancy is dated from the first day of your last period, although you conceived about two weeks later.

EDD chart (above)
To find your expected date of delivery, look at the first day of your last period on the top line of figures – your EDD appears in bold type underneath.

Week 5

MON

TUES

WED

THURS

FRI

SAT

SUN

Notes

▪ YOU AND YOUR DEVELOPING BABY

You Week 5 is the first week that a urine test (which works by detecting a particular pregnancy hormone in your urine) would give you a positive result. The most likely sign of pregnancy is a missed period although you might mistake a little 'breakthrough bleeding', which sometimes occurs, for an ordinary period. Other early signs of pregnancy that you may experience at some stage in the next few weeks are outlined in Week 4.

Baby Your baby's nervous system, spine and brain are already beginning to develop, and the cells which started off as an embryonic disc grow lengthways until your baby has a definite head and tail end.

The first stage in the development of the central nervous system is the formation of a groove in the top layer of cells towards the tail end of the embryo. The cells fold up and round to make the hollow neural tube, one end of which will become your baby's brain and the other end his spinal cord. At the same time blocks of tissue begin to grow which will eventually form your baby's spine, ribs and abdominal muscles.

During Week 5 your baby is shorter than your eyelashes – about 2mm (¹⁄₁₀in) – but he is rapidly developing his major component parts.

Star signs

Now you know approximately what date your baby is due, you might like to look at the star signs and see what characteristics he is likely to have – and what you might be letting yourself in for in terms of his possible future temperament!

The descriptions below are just little teasers. If you want an astrologer to tell you your baby's real character, and even possibly his future, you will need to know the exact time of his birth. Ask the midwife to keep an eye on the clock.

See Week 1 for kits for Pregnancy Tests

Capricorn
22 December–20 January
Serious, materialistic and ambitious, they rise through the ranks, but resist inner change. They are anxious for social prestige to bolster their ego, but always remain steadfast and reliable.

Aquarius
21 January–18 February
Cerebral, intellectual, detached, they are the inventors and theoreticians of the ideal – although their ideals can be fairly fickle. They generate goodwill, friendship – and change.

Pisces
19 February–20 March
Innately psychic and finely attuned, both to the needs of living things and to music and poetry. They are liable to be injured, by their own need to be needed, and by dreamers of other dreams.

Aries
21 March–20 April
Hot-tempered, passionate and aggressive; in battle, brave, indomitable and enthusiastic; likely to be either a trouble-maker or an initiator. Either way, he'll make sure he comes first.

Taurus
21 April–21 May
Down-to-earth and sensual. They are sometimes slow starters, but always thorough. Taureans can be stubborn and possessive but are usually mild-tempered – except when they see red . . .

Gemini
22 May–June 21
Versatile, verbal, mercurial – often concise and witty. They are usually as clever with their hands as with their tongues. Expect an intrepid traveller with an inquiring nature.

Cancer
22 June–22 July
Protective, nurturing, emotional; worriers; keepers of the past and of the familial dwelling. Not over-ambitious, your crab will give anything for a quiet, cosy life.

Leo
23 July–23 August
Dramatic, charismatic, leonine. Warm-hearted and friendly, especially to those who appreciate them. You'll recognize your little Leo by his mane of hair and the way he purrs at himself in the mirror.

Virgo
24 August–22 September
Practical and hypercritical but well-intentioned; purist, perfectionist, perceptive – and tireless tidiers up. Always anxious to please, baby Virgo will bring you tea in bed in the morning.

Libra
23 September–23 October
Attractive, tactful and poised. Innately artistic and such a sense of fairness, or indecision, that it is impossible for them not to take both sides of an argument.

Scorpio
24 October–22 November
Secretive; jealous, demanding, revengeful and forever loyal once you are friendly; a real ability to get to the bottom of things . . . Scorpios are possibly a little paranoid.

Sagittarius
23 November–21 December
Adventurous, both mentally and physically; expansive, sometimes over-indulgent, but philosophical and good-natured, with an open-door policy.

Week 6

Month: Dates:

MON

TUES

WED

THURS

FRI

SAT

SUN

Notes

You Whether or not you have done a pregnancy test at home, using a kit, you should at this stage visit your doctor to confirm your pregnancy. By now your uterus can be felt to be swollen and slightly enlarged – it is about the size of a tangerine.

Baby Although your baby's face still can't be made out, he already has a neck, a completed rudimentary brain and a bump for a head. The formation of the head is rapidly followed by the abdominal and chest cavities. In the chest cavity a heart is developing, which as yet has only two chambers instead of four.

This week the connecting stalk by which the embryo has been attached to your placenta begins to grow into the umbilical cord and blood vessels start forming within it, strengthening the link between you and your child. By the end of the week your baby has a bloodstream with a functioning circulation. Tiny limb buds appear at the corners of his body.

The lower part of the body is still comparatively undeveloped and looks more like a tail. Another shaping feature is that the blocks of tissue that make up the back of the embryo develop faster than those of the front, causing him to grow in a curved shape, resembling a seahorse.

By the end of this week your baby will be 6mm (¼in) long – the size of your little fingernail.

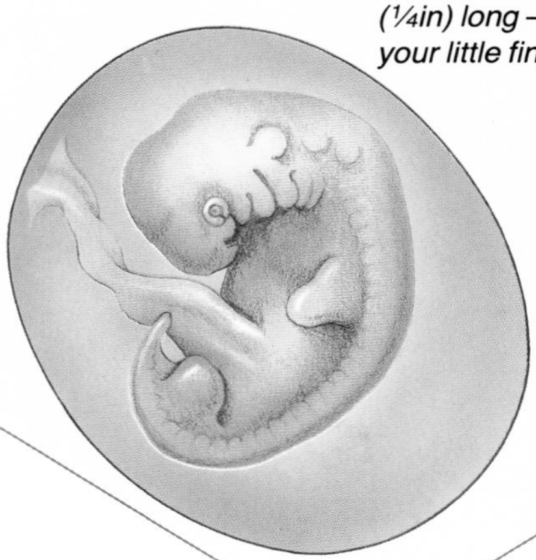

DON'T FORGET First doctor's visit to confirm your pregnancy.

Your relationship

If you have had a miscarriage or difficult pregnancies in the past or are experiencing vaginal bleeding now, ask your doctor's advice about sexual intercourse during the first fourteen weeks. The only other times not to have sex are at the very end of your pregnancy, either if you have a show (i.e. your plug of mucus is dislodged) or if your waters break. Otherwise there is no reason why you shouldn't have sexual intercourse throughout your pregnancy.

The only thing never to do in pregnancy is for your partner to blow into your vagina – this could lead to blood clots (embolism).

What if I feel frigid...?
The human female is one of the very few mammals to permit sexual intercourse at any time during pregnancy so it is not surprising if sometimes you don't feel like sex. If you do feel frigid during your pregnancy, don't worry – your desire will return later. A fairly typical pattern in pregnancy is for your sex drive to decrease in the first fourteen weeks then increase again in your second trimester (Weeks 14–27); you may lose interest in sex after about Week 29, as you get larger, more tired and uncomfortable.

See Week 1 for kits for Pregnancy Tests

See Week 4 for Your Due Date

See Week 9 for Antenatal Care

See Week 24 for Sex in Later Pregnancy

Seeing your doctor
You may not want to tell the world that you're pregnant just yet. But you must tell your doctor so that she can confirm your pregnancy and start you thinking about antenatal care.

Many women in fact feel highly sensual during pregnancy, especially during the second trimester. Your change in libido may be due to the high level of hormones circulating in your blood. During pregnancy your sexual organs are more highly developed and many parts of your body are more sensitive and therefore more capable of arousal. Sex could also be more fun now because it can be spontaneous – there's no worry about birth control or wondering whether this will lead to a longed-for baby.

Sexual superstitions
Contrary to what you or your partner may believe, it is impossible for his penis, or the semen which he ejaculates, to harm your baby. The muscles of the cervix and a special plug of mucus seal off your uterus completely. Where there is a risk (see above), the miscarriage could be triggered off by your orgasm causing your uterus to contract, which might set off other contractions. But this will not happen in a normal pregnancy.

First doctor's visit
You will be asked for the date of the first day of your last menstrual period, so that the date your baby is due can be worked out. You should take with you a sample of the first urine you passed that morning so that a pregnancy test can be done.

You will also be asked in which hospital you wish to have your baby, so that you can be booked in. If you want your baby to be born at home, your doctor will arrange for you to see the midwife who will care for you during pregnancy and deliver you.

You will also have to decide where you want your antenatal check-ups. If you are having your baby in hospital you may decide to go there for all your check-ups. Alternatively, you could opt for 'shared care', where your doctor and the hospital take it in turns to look after you. This familiarizes you with the hospital and keeps you in contact with your doctor.

Week 7

Month: Dates:

MON

TUES

WED

THURS

FRI

SAT

SUN

Notes

YOU AND YOUR DEVELOPING BABY

You You may feel dizzy or faint if you stand for long periods. You may also have fits of overwhelming tiredness, which is normal. Go to bed earlier at night and, if possible, rest during the day. By now you may be experiencing some of pregnancy's 'problems', including some emotional ones.

Baby Week 7 is when many begin to call the embryo a fetus. Although your baby's head still has some strange-looking lumps and is still at an unusual angle to its body, being bent forward on its chest, it is beginning to assume its eventual human shape. The limb buds are growing rapidly and arms and legs starting to resemble paddle-shapes.

The ears and eyes are developing and apertures for the nostrils are appearing. Development of the jaws and mouth is continuing and the lips, tongue and first teeth buds are now visible.

By the end of this week your baby's brain and spinal cord will be almost complete. The heart, although still a simple structure, now has four chambers. It is beating with enough force to circulate blood cells through the complex network of blood vessels that extends into the head and throughout the body.

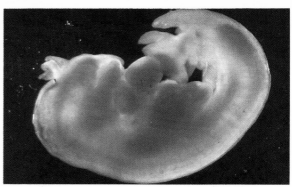

Your baby is now about the size of your thumbnail.

DON'T FORGET Start investigating antenatal classes (See Week 29) now.

18

Mixed emotions

You will be coming to terms with what it means to be pregnant. From initial excitement or nervousness, your feelings may be settling into a state of contentment. It is up to you when you announce to the world that you are pregnant. Some want to broadcast the news as soon as the pregnancy is confirmed, while others prefer to wait until they are sure all is well, after three months or so.

The first trimester may well be the worst time of your pregnancy, emotionally as well as physically. You have just taken a step into the unknown which is, let's face it, quite courageous. No matter how much you may have wanted a baby in the past, you may now be wondering if you've made the right decision. Possibly for the first time in your life, you are also being forced into a constant awareness of your body which may be making you feel sick, tired and over-emotional. You may also be a bit nervous that you are going to miscarry.

It can seem that you are surrounded by pregnant women, and you may find everyone will want to tell you their pregnancy stories. Listen if you want to and don't if you prefer not. Always trust your own instincts.

Allaying your fears
It's quite normal to worry about whether your baby is going to be all right and whether anything you're doing might harm him. Thankfully only a tiny percentage of babies born today are handicapped. It is important to behave sensibly throughout your pregnancy; keep all your doctor's appointments and never be afraid to ask for medical advice on anything that is worrying you (see Week 9): remember that you're asking for your baby as well as for yourself. Cut down on any risks to your baby such as smoking or drinking (see Week 2).

Most women are worried about labour. Dreams about giving birth to weird objects are common. You may find it helps sharing your fears about labour with your friends or your doctor or midwife. On a broader level, you may feel worried about how the baby is going to change your life, both financially and socially. Will it end your freedom?

Disrupt the happy relationship you have with your partner? You may wonder how you will cope with bringing up a child. Note down your anxieties and feelings in this diary – you'll be amazed how the worries increase and decrease in importance during the weeks ahead. Never let a problem get on top of you – find someone to discuss it with.

At times during your pregnancy you may have the sense of being very alone and feel that your partner isn't doing enough. You may argue more during pregnancy, but you will also feel closer. Much of this can be put down to changing hormones. It is important to involve your partner as early as you can.

See Weeks 11 and 12 for Common Problems

See Week 23 for The Father's Role

Morning sickness
By now you may have begun to feel sick. Nausea, and sometimes actual vomiting, affects about half of all pregnant women and you may feel sick at any time, day or night. The cause is thought to be related to the hormonal changes taking place in your body. Morning sickness is not serious, just very unpleasant, but with luck it will disappear around the twelfth to fourteenth week – let your doctor know if you are still nauseous after Week 14.

If you can't keep anything down, not even drinks, tell your doctor. But otherwise, try to alleviate the symptoms and reduce the risk of being sick. Here are some suggestions that may help.
- ☐ Eat a biscuit before getting out of bed in the morning and get up slowly.
- ☐ Have a bowl of cereal and milk before you go to sleep.
- ☐ Eat small, light meals – as many as you need – throughout the day. Try half a baked potato or sipping soda water as stomach settlers.
- ☐ Drink fluids between meals rather than with food.
- ☐ Wear clothes without waistbands.
- ☐ Put away anything that makes you feel sick, such as soaps or perfume.
- ☐ If cooking smells make you nauseous, buy foods that don't need preparing.

19

Week 8

Month: Dates:

MON

TUES

WED

THURS

FRI

SAT

SUN

Notes

You You may already start to notice your body changing. Your waist may be vanishing, and your breasts and nipples will be enlarging.

Baby Week 8 is an important time for the growth of your baby's eyes and inner ear. At the moment the eyes are covered by a skin which will eventually split to form eyelids. His ears are visible but not yet protruding. The middle part of the ear, responsible for balance as well as hearing, will have developed by the end of the week. During the next seven days he will start to open his mouth and be able to suck and chew once the upper and lower jaws fuse at the sides.

By now his heart is pumping vigorously with a regular rhythm. Blood vessels can be seen through the skin which is as thin as tracing paper. All the major internal organs (heart, brain, lungs, kidneys, liver and gut) are now in place although not yet fully developed.

The bones of his arms and legs are starting to harden and elongate; fingers and toes are more obvious though joined by webs of skin; and the major joints (shoulders, elbows, hips and knees) are forming.

At present your baby is still smaller than your nose – 2.5cm (1in) long – and fish-like in shape, with an over-large head and small body.

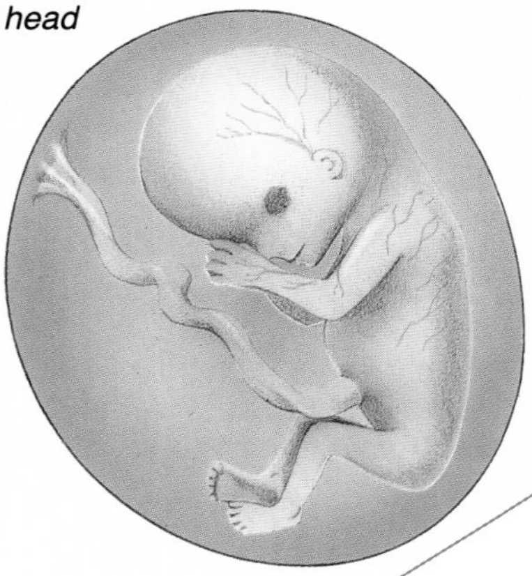

■ **DON'T FORGET** Make a dental appointment. Buy a support bra soon.

Looking good

A good diet, plus plenty of rest and sleep, are extremely important throughout pregnancy. Experiment with make-up and different hairstyles if you want people to look at your face rather than your stomach. You may well find you look better than ever over the next few months.

Hair Both hair and nails grow more rapidly than usual. Dry hair may become drier and greasy hair greasier. Don't experiment with perms or colour just now. Short hair is more manageable and easier to wash.

Nails Nails may break or split easily. Keep them short and wear gloves for any chores. Try rubbing baby oil into the base of your nails nightly to help prevent cracking, and eat more dairy products.

Breasts Don't use soap on your breasts. To toughen your nipples before breast-feeding, try splashing your breasts every morning with lots of cold water or rubbing your nipples daily with a flannel. Buy two new support bras (see below).

Skin Most women's skin improves but if yours does the opposite, don't worry – after pregnancy it will be back to normal. The extra blood circulating round your body will make you look rosy-cheeked and 'blooming'. Use moisturizer but not foundation creams; let the new colour of your skin shine through.

Stretch marks These may occur if the elastic fibres in your skin have become over-stretched and ruptured. Although they first appear as dramatic reddish streaks, they shrink to indistinct silvery lines afterwards. There is no sure way to avoid stretch marks. It helps not to put on too much weight and to maintain a correct posture. Applying special body creams will also help to keep your skin supple. You can get support for your abdomen from a lightweight pregnancy corset.

Colour changes Pigmented birthmarks and freckles can darken during pregnancy, especially if exposed to sunlight. They will lighten again after delivery. Some women may get blotchy patches on their face and neck; these are caused by pregnancy hormones. Use make-up to cover them up if they worry you. They will start to disappear after delivery.

Teeth During pregnancy the gums around your teeth become spongier and more prone to infection – you may notice them bleeding more. Avoid sugary foods, brush your teeth at least twice a day and floss them regularly. Make an appointment with your dentist now: dental treatment is free for pregnant women.

Personal hygiene You may find you sweat more, due to an increase in body weight and temperature. Wash regularly and wear cotton underwear if possible; use talcum powder after washing. Never douche during pregnancy.

Buying a new bra

Your breasts may increase by as much as two bra sizes during pregnancy. Since breasts contain no muscular tissue, they need good support or they may never return to their normal shape.

It is a good idea to go to a shop where staff are trained to fit bras. They should have wide shoulder straps and adjustable backs to allow for later chest expansion. Make sure they are the right cup size.

21

Week 9

Month: _____   Dates: _____

MON

TUES

WED

THURS

FRI

SAT

SUN

Notes

You You may begin to notice skin changes caused by pregnancy hormones. Any wrinkles may become less obvious due to your face fattening out. Your gums may also be thickening. Gingivitis or gum infection is more common during pregnancy (see Week 8). Start some regular exercise; go walking or swimming every day if possible, though avoid swimming around the time you would normally be expecting your period. Diving is not recommended during pregnancy.

Baby Your baby is beginning to have a more mature appearance although his head is still bent forward on his chest. The development of his eyes is now complete, although each eye still has a membrane eyelid over it. A nose has also appeared.

During Week 9 the chest cavity becomes separated from the abdominal cavity by a band of muscle that later develops into the diaphragm, a muscle that plays an important role in breathing. The spine is making its first, tiny movements and, although you won't be able to feel it yet, your baby is starting to kick and move around in order to exercise his muscles.

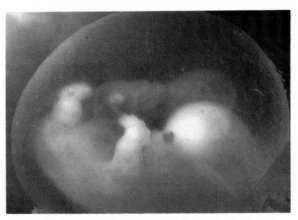

The fastest growth this week is in the limbs, hands and feet. Fingers and toes start to be defined.

Antenatal care

Your first antenatal check-up will probably be any time from now until Week 15. No matter what you may feel, or how busy you are, antenatal hospital and doctor visits are time well spent. It is essential to give your baby the best start in life by regular checks that all is well. They also give you an opportunity to see inside the hospital in which your baby will be born and to ask questions about their procedures. Later on you can ask to see the labour wards and the delivery room.

Write down everything you want to discuss with your doctor or midwife before every visit – it is easy to forget things once you are there (pregnancy amnesia is famous!). If they are short of time, ask when you can come back for a discussion. It is important that you find answers to everything that is worrying you. Take notes of the discussion or you may forget what the doctor said.

Think about the kind of birth you want before you start talking to your doctor about it. Read books about childbirth and talk to friends about the birth of their children. It is most important that you are happy when giving birth.

Below is a list of questions you may wish to ask. They apply mainly to hospital deliveries.

See
Week 35 for
Pain Relief

See
Week 40 for
The Birth

See page 88
for
Understanding
your Hospital
Notes

Antenatal check-ups
You will be weighed at each visit, to check that your baby is growing satisfactorily and that you are not putting on too much weight. Your blood pressure will be measured each time and a sample of urine tested. You keep a copy of your hospital notes.

Questions for the doctor or hospital

Antenatal care
- [ ] How often will I have antenatal appointments?
- [ ] What tests will you be giving me?
- [ ] Where can I go for antenatal classes?
- [ ] Will I be shown around the labour and postnatal wards before the birth?

The birth
- [ ] Is my partner (or close relative or friend) welcome all the time during labour?
- [ ] Will they ever be asked to leave the room? If so, why?
- [ ] What is your policy on induction, pain relief, episiotomy, routine monitoring?
- [ ] Is an epidural available?
- [ ] Do you automatically shave my pubic hair or give me an enema?
- [ ] Can I walk around in labour and find my own position for birth?
- [ ] If I need to have a Caesarean section can my partner stay with me? Can it be done with an epidural?
- [ ] Will my baby be put to my breast immediately after birth?
- [ ] Is it possible to be alone with my baby and partner immediately after the birth?

The hospital
- [ ] Do you have a Special Baby Unit? If not, where is the nearest one?
- [ ] Do you have a birthing chair, a birthing pool (or any other equipment you want to know about)?
- [ ] Is it possible to have my baby born in subdued lighting and a quiet atmosphere?
- [ ] What is the normal length of stay on the postnatal ward?
- [ ] How many beds are there to a ward?
- [ ] What are visiting hours?
- [ ] Are there any special rules about visiting or about numbers of visitors?

Week 10

Month: Dates:

MON

TUES

WED

THURS

FRI

SAT

SUN

Notes

You Your uterus has now grown to the size of an orange but is still hidden away within your pelvis. Your heart, lungs and kidneys are also beginning to work harder; start watching your diet (see Week 3) particularly carefully. Your breasts will be noticeably larger by now and can be rather tender.

Baby During the last four weeks your baby's brain has developed so rapidly that his head is still large in proportion to the rest of his body. By the end of this week the inner part of the ears are complete and the external parts are beginning to grow.

The lungs are growing inside the chest cavity and, in the abdomen, the stomach and intestine are formed and the kidneys are moving into their permanent positions. The umbilical cord is properly formed and blood is circulating along it.

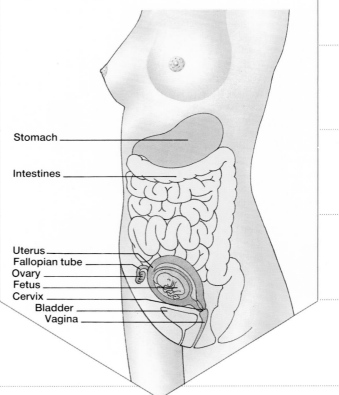

Stomach

Intestines

Uterus
Fallopian tube
Ovary
Fetus
Cervix
Bladder
Vagina

DON'T FORGET Find out now about your legal and financial rights.

Working in pregnancy

One positive advantage of working during pregnancy is that it takes your mind off waiting. But if your job is potentially dangerous (involving a lot of bending or heavy lifting, contact with chemicals, lead, dangerous substances or X-rays), it is best to discuss with your doctor and employer about how safe it is to continue. If it normally involves a lot of standing, see if you can switch to a more sedentary job for the time

being. If there is *any* medical reason why you should stop work, then do, but remember that you will need a doctor's certificate. If you have any problems with your employer, try and get legal help (see below).

Sleepiness may make it impossible for you to concentrate during early pregnancy. For many this is the most difficult time in which to work. Don't push yourself – this feeling of exhaustion will only last for another few weeks. If you find yourself dropping off to sleep during the day, you need rest. Try and take some time off work until you feel less tired. Nausea may also make it hard to concentrate. Bring in food to pick at during the day to stop you feeling sick and make sure you have a good breakfast.

If you are working full-time, you are allowed to take time off work to attend regular check-ups and antenatal classes. You will also be entitled to maternity leave once you have your baby. Talk to your employer or trade union representative about this and about the payments to which you are entitled.

Working after childbirth
Around this time you should start thinking about whether you do want to return to work (either full- or part-time) after you have had your baby and, if you do, how long you want to take on maternity leave. Discuss all this with your partner and, subsequently, your employer. It is wise to confirm your arrangements in writing.

See Week 7 for Morning Sickness

Benefits and entitlements
As a pregnant woman and, later, as a mother, you are entitled to certain rights and benefits, depending partly on your financial, employment and marital circumstances. Finding out about them may appear complicated, but in the first instance you should get hold of information leaflet FB8, available from a post office. Your local Department of Health and Social Security, Citizens' Advice Bureau or legal aid centre will be able to help you clear up any uncertainties you have or with any form-filling you need to do.

Bringing up children?
A guide to benefits for families with children

Babies and benefits
A guide to benefits for expectant and new mothers

Week 11

Month: Dates:

MON

TUES

WED

THURS

FRI

SAT

SUN

Notes

You If you've been feeling sick during the last few weeks you may begin to feel better. Start thinking about where you want to go for antenatal classes and book now as they often fill up early (see Week 29).

Baby By the end of the week all your baby's essential internal organs will be formed and the majority beginning to function. From now on, these organs will simply continue to grow in size. From the end of Week 11, therefore, your baby is relatively safe from the risk of developing major congenital abnormalities.

His head is still relatively large for his body size and his limbs are still quite short and thin. His ankles and wrists have formed and his elbows and knees are taking shape.

By the end of this week, however, he is clearly recognizable as a small human baby. His face is also beginning to look more human as it becomes more rounded. The back of the head has enlarged, so that his eyes are in a more natural position; his ears look flatter and continue to develop.

Your baby's heart is pumping blood to all parts of the body as well as through the umbilical cord to what will eventually become the placenta.

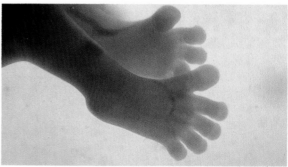

Your baby's fingers and toes are now separate and clearly developed.

■ **DON'T FORGET** Go and see your dentist if you haven't already.

Common problems/1

Most of the problems mentioned here and in Week 12 are fairly common in early pregnancy and are more of a nuisance than serious. Speak to your doctor immediately, however, if you experience any of the problems highlighted in the panel.

Backache See Week 31
Bladder problems In early and late pregnancy you need to pass urine more frequently, sometimes to the extent that it wakes you up at night. You could try drinking less in the evening and rocking back and forwards as you pass urine, which lessens the pressure on your bladder and may help empty it more completely. Talk to your doctor if you have pain or blood when passing urine. (See also Cystitis below)
Bleeding gums This can be a sign of gum infection (gingivitis). Pregnancy is an important time for dental hygiene (see Week 8). Massage your gums with fingertips before brushing your teeth, using a soft bristle brush. See your dentist.
Blocked nose Your nose may be more stuffed-up than usual, especially on waking up. Don't blow your nose too hard and don't use a nasal spray or take cold cures for it. Avoid dusty atmospheres and try menthol or plain steam inhalations. Your blocked nose will probably disappear after childbirth if not before. (See also Nose bleeds, Week 12)
Constipation This may last throughout your pregnancy, due to the hormone progesterone causing your intestinal muscles to relax,

Contact the doctor if you:
- [ ] Are vomiting excessively.
- [ ] Have abdominal cramps.
- [ ] Have any vaginal bleeding apart from around the time of your first missed period.
- [ ] Have any leak of clear fluid from your vagina.
- [ ] Fall or have an accident.
- [ ] Have swollen feet, fingers, ankles or face.
- [ ] Are short of breath.
- [ ] Have excessive dizziness or headaches.
- [ ] Don't notice any fetal movements for twenty-four hours or more.
- [ ] Have excessive white or discoloured discharge.

which slows down your bowel movements. Drink lots of water and fruit juice and eat bran and wholemeal bread. Avoid strong laxatives and empty your bowels the moment you feel you need to: too much straining could lead to piles (see Week 12).
Cramp Cramp may be due to poor blood circulation, lack of salt in the diet or having hot milky drinks before bed. It usually occurs in your legs. If it happens at night, try hopping on the foot of the affected leg or massaging it firmly for a while – or stretch the affected part, then quickly bend it. Make sure your bedding is loose.

If you get a lot of cramp, try going for a short walk or try and stretch your calf muscles by exercising your legs in some other way before you go to bed to get the circulation going. Your doctor may give you calcium supplements.

Cystitis (bladder infection) If you have a burning feeling when passing urine and you feel as if you have to pass water all the time, you may have cystitis. See your doctor immediately and drink as much water or barley water as you can.
Fainting During early and late pregnancy you may feel dizzy or unsteady and may even faint, due to the brain being relatively deprived of blood, because your blood is rushing either to your feet (if you are standing) or to your uterus. If you feel faint get into fresh air as soon as possible, loosen tight clothes and sit down or, if possible, lie down with your head flat and your legs raised. Don't lock the bathroom door if you are at home.

Avoid standing for long periods, having hot baths, sitting in smoky atmospheres and getting up too quickly from a sitting or lying position. Try increasing your iron intake (see Week 19).
Flatulence This is due to a sluggish intestine during pregnancy. Flatulence is caused either by you swallowing air (often to stop yourself feeling sick) or eating certain foods (like pulses, fried foods, cabbage, onions and peppers). Avoid problem foods where possible and eat light meals.
Haemorrhoids See Piles
Headaches Try not to worry if you get occasional headaches; rest and relaxation help. If your headaches are frequent, tell your doctor – it may be a sign of high blood pressure.
Incontinence See Week 24
Indigestion and heartburn See Week 24

See Week 24 for Problems of Later Pregnancy

(Continued in Week 12)

Week 12

Month: Dates:

MON

TUES

WED

THURS

FRI

SAT

SUN

Notes

▪ YOU AND YOUR DEVELOPING BABY

You Your uterus can now be felt as a hard ridge above your pubic bone, although you may not yet know what you are feeling for. From the beginning of this week you will probably start putting on serious weight. About a quarter of your pregnancy weight gain will take place from now until Week 20 (see Week 25). Most women gain 7–14kg (15–30lb). If you are underweight now, you may need to put on more than 14kg (30lb). If you are overweight, it may be a good idea to discuss a diet with your doctor to make sure you put on less than 14kg (30lb) (see Week 3). Never start an unsupervised slimming campaign while pregnant.

Baby Although few muscles are working, your baby is already using the muscles that will be used in breathing after birth. His brain and muscles are co-ordinating so that he is kicking, curling his toes, rotating his feet and wrists, clenching and unclenching his fists, pressing his lips together, frowning and making other facial expressions.

This week the umbilical cord starts to circulate blood between the fetus and the group of membranes attached to the wall of your uterus. Your baby begins to rely on these membranes for nourishment and the placenta (or afterbirth) now begins to function.

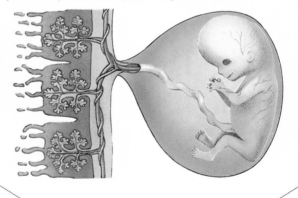

Common problems/2

Insomnia Don't worry about not sleeping; it's more important that you relax. Try the usual tricks – a warm milk drink at bedtime (unless you are suffering from cramp); reading a good book; having a warm bath; relaxation exercises (see Week 33). If insomnia becomes a problem, talk to your doctor about it – don't take sleeping pills without advice.

Itching and skin problems General itching – with or without a rash – can be due to poor hygiene, excess weight gain and/or sweating. Keep your body clean and apply calamine lotion or talcum powder to the affected area. Try and keep cool – wear loose clothing (no waistbands) made of natural fibres. Any tiny red spots, or naevi, in your skin are harmless and will disappear.

Morning sickness See Week 7

Nose bleeds During pregnancy there is an increased volume of blood in your body, including in the vessels lining your nose. Nose bleeds can easily occur if you blow your nose too hard and the vessels rupture. If you are subject to nose-bleeding, try breathing through your mouth and avoid blowing your nose violently. If your nose starts bleeding, lean forward slightly and apply gently pressure to the bridge of your nose, or pinch your nostrils together to stop the blood flow.

Piles (haemorrhoids) Piles are a form of varicose vein which occur around the anus. You may first notice some discomfort and possibly some bleeding when your bowels are opened. Piles can be caused by anything that increases pressure in your abdomen such as constipation, chronic coughing or lifting. They can be very uncomfortable, especially when passing stools, and they may itch and bleed slightly especially if the pile is large and outside your rectum. Cure your constipation (see Week 11) and try to keep your stools soft and regular. Keep your anal area clean to avoid irritation and ask your doctor for creams or suppositories if you need help.

If your piles itch badly, put some crushed ice in a plastic bag, cover it with a cloth and hold the pack gently against the piles. Piles usually go within a week or two of delivery.

Pins and needles See Week 24

Stretch marks See Week 8

Sweating Wash frequently and use talcum powder. Wear natural fibres and drink more to replace lost fluids.

Swelling of legs, ankles, fingers (Oedema) See Week 24

Thrush Thrush is common during pregnancy and can be passed on to your baby, although this can be quickly cleared up by a course of medicine. Don't wear tights or knickers that are too tight; ask your doctor for creams and pessaries to clear up the infection.

Tiredness This may go on throughout pregnancy although it often gets better in your second trimester.

Vaginal secretions An increase in vaginal secretions is normal during pregnancy due to the change in vaginal tissues in preparation for the birth. If your secretions smell awful, make you sore, are painful or contain blood, tell your doctor. Otherwise, if you need to, wear a sanitary towel (not a tampon) and in any case wear cotton underwear and wash often. Never douche or use a vaginal deodorant during pregnancy. Make sure you don't have thrush (see above).

Varicose veins Varicose veins can be inherited or caused by hormones or, in later pregnancy, by your enlarged womb pressing down and obstructing the flow of blood from your legs to your heart.

Avoid standing or sitting still for long periods, crossing your legs, wearing tight garments or being constipated. If varicose veins do run in the family, wear support tights or stockings from an early stage.

To prevent varicose veins, exercise frequently, watch your weight and rest every day with legs raised above your heart.

See Week 24 for Problems of Later Pregnancy

It is most important to rest when you feel tired in pregnancy.

Week 13

Month: Dates:

MON

TUES

WED

THURS

FRI

SAT

SUN

Notes

YOU AND YOUR DEVELOPING BABY

You From now on your uterus will be enlarging at a noticeable rate. It is already swollen by your pregnancy and measures approximately 10cm (4in) in diameter. Your doctor will be able to feel it in your lower abdomen as a soft swelling coming out of your pelvis.

The main danger of miscarriage is over. From now on syphilis, rubella (German measles) and rare tropical diseases are the only known infections which can cross to the fetus and do him any harm.

You may see a dark line (the *linea nigra*) appearing down the centre of your abdomen. This continues to darken during pregnancy but will fade after delivery.

Baby By the end of this week your baby is properly formed. But were he to be born, he could not survive because, although all the organs are present, they have not yet matured enough to perform the jobs for which they are intended. The rest of your pregnancy is designed to allow the fetus to grow in size, and to give his vital organs sufficient time to mature so that they are capable of independent life.

His neck is now fully developed, which allows his head to move freely on his body. His face is formed, with mouth, nose and external ears properly developed.

By the end of this week your baby is 7.5cm (3in) long and weighs 28g (1oz). He has plenty of room to move within the amniotic sac.

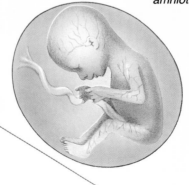

Homoeopathy and herbs

Homoeopathy works by treating the person as a whole, allowing for both emotional and physical states of being rather than by just treating individual physical symptoms. The remedies are made from natural substances which aim to stimulate your body's healing powers into healing itself. Homoeopaths claim that homoeopathy really comes into its own during pregnancy as the pregnant body is particularly able to heal itself (wounds heal twice as fast during pregnancy).

There are homoeopathic aids for pregnancy and for after the birth. Consult a professional homoeopath if you are interested in taking any remedies but always tell your orthodox doctor about these. Below is a brief guide to what is available.

Aesculus (horse chestnut): can be used in cream or suppository form to relieve piles.
Arnica tablets: may be helpful during and after labour to reduce bruising and make the pelvic floor area more comfortable. Also helps with exhaustion.
Arsenicum album: may help to solve digestive problems.
Calendula tincture: can be taken after delivery to soothe and heal perineal tears and episiotomy cuts.
Carbo Veg: a homoeopathic charcoal which helps with indigestion and wind.
Caulophyllum: taken regularly, starting a few weeks before the birth, this can help improve the muscle tone of the uterus. During labour, it can help your cervix dilate and help ease painful contractions.
Ipecacuanha: helps to reduce nausea.
Mercurius: helps to stop diarrhoea.
Phosphorus: can help to relieve nausea.

Herbs during pregnancy
If you don't feel like drinking coffee or ordinary tea at the moment, you may wish to try herbal teas. Make a herbal brew exactly as you would a pot of tea, only leave it to brew for ten minutes. To make a cup, use one teaspoon of herbs (available from a herbalist) per cup of boiling water.

Some herbs are healing agents, others have a relaxing effect, some just taste good. Most herbs and herbal teas (especially pre-packaged ones) cannot harm you if taken in moderation, but some do have an unwanted action on the pregnant uterus so it is best to check with a pharmacist who sells herbal remedies or a specialist herbal retailer. Herbs, such as sage, marjoram and parsley, are only safe during pregnancy in the amounts used in cooking. It is important to avoid southernwood which is used as a tonic to reduce menstrual flow and also feverfew and gentian which can induce abortion.

Herbal remedies for problems of pregnancy

Indigestion Try a mixture of comfrey root, marshmallow root, meadowsweet and dandelion root; fennel is a mild laxative that can also relieve painful wind; hop tea will smooth muscle tensions affecting digestive and bowel functions.

Insomnia Try drinking camomile tea, hop tea or lime blossom tea just before bed.

Labour Raspberry leaf tea and squaw vine tea both relax the muscles in your uterus and ease labour. Drink a cup a day in the last three months of pregnancy, but avoid earlier consumption of raspberry leaf tea as this can lead to premature labour.

Mineral and vitamin deficiency Nettle tea is rich in iron and minerals. Rosehips are rich in Vitamin C.

Morning sickness Hop tea or black hawhound help relieve morning sickness; peppermint and spearmint ease sickness and help with digestion.

Week 14

Month: Dates:

MON

TUES

WED

THURS

FRI

SAT

SUN

Notes

■ YOU AND YOUR DEVELOPING BABY

You You are beginning the middle stage of your pregnancy, generally thought of as the most enjoyable. During the next fourteen weeks you will probably feel better, more creative and more energetic, as well as more positive about your new baby, than at any other stage of pregnancy. Your uterus is now the size of a large grapefruit and you should be able to feel the top of it two fingers' breadth above your pubic bone.

Baby Week 14 is the beginning of the second trimester, the stage of the main growth of your baby; he increases in size, his organs mature and complex hormone and other processes develop.

Your baby has begun to grow hair: he has eyebrows and a small amount of hair on his head. His heart is beating strongly and can be heard using an ultrasonic device. His heartbeat is almost twice the rate of a normal adult's. All his major muscles are responding to stimulation from the brain. The arms can bend from the wrist and elbow, the fingers can curl, make fists and grasp: his nervous system has begun to function.

Your placenta is now fully operational; it both nourishes your fetus and produces hormones. Your child starts to drink some amniotic fluid and his kidneys begin to make a little urine which he can now pass.

During the last seven days your baby has more than doubled in weight. He now weighs 65g (2¼oz) and measures about 10cm (4in).

Other children

Looking after children is one of the most exhausting occupations for a pregnant woman. Learn to pick up your child with your knees bent, or kneel down to cuddle and comfort him instead of picking him up. Make an effort to stay cool, calm and collected, especially during early pregnancy, and try not to let your attitude to your older children change.

If possible, don't talk about your pregnancy to your children too soon or they will get bored with waiting. Only once they have noticed, should they be told that a baby is growing inside your tummy. Later on, go through this diary with them week by week, and let them feel him kicking inside you.

Prepare children by pointing out babies in their prams in the street – comment on how helpless they look so that the new baby is not expected to be a playmate from the start. Show older children pictures of themselves as babies and buy them dolls of their own so they have someone to look after too. Shortly before the event, take them to buy their new sibling a present. If you need a child to move

out of his familiar cot, or room, do it well before the baby is born so that the two events do not appear related. Let your partner increase his involvement with your children, especially with bathing, feeding and story-telling, so that you can decrease yours well before the birth.

The middle term of pregnancy
Emotions The middle period of pregnancy is usually a time for feeling positive, energetic and creative. You may begin to feel closer to other women and find yourself talking about personal things you haven't discussed before. You may love the attention you will begin receiving from other people once they notice your bump.

The first time your baby kicks can be very exciting and may bring you much closer to him. It's the first real sign that someone separate from you is there, and that something really is happening.

Working Your excess energy can make you overdo things during your working day. No matter how strong you feel, take it easy whenever you can. Skip lunch dates and lunchtime shopping expeditions: instead bring in a salad and sandwich for lunch. Don't stand all day – this may lead to circulation problems and varicose veins later on. Put your feet up when you can – rest them on the drawer of your filing cabinet or on your wastepaper basket. Try squatting instead of bending over which might strain your back. Always ask for help – people are happy to give it.

Involving older children
Children should be encouraged to want a brother or sister and, later, to care for the new baby so that they feel involved rather than resentful. Inform and involve them in your pregnancy too, according to their age and how much they can understand.

If you are having the baby in hospital, make arrangements for your children well in advance and rehearse their timetables and movements frequently; it is only surprise that will worry them. When you leave for hospital, say goodbye to them no matter what time of day or night it is. It is upsetting for children to wake up and find you gone.

If you want a home birth, your children will be involved right from the start. Tell them what is going to happen beforehand.

33

Week 15

MON

TUES

WED

THURS

FRI

SAT

SUN

Notes

YOU AND YOUR DEVELOPING BABY

You Your clothes are probably getting too tight for you and you will need to wear looser garments. Your pregnancy may even begin to show, though this varies a lot from person to person. To cope with the increased amount of blood circulating in your body and your baby's need for oxygen, your enlarged heart has increased its output by twenty per cent. You're probably beginning to feel more energetic, so think about going on holiday sometime during the next ten weeks.

Baby From now on most of your baby's energy is directed towards growing and maturing. The hair on his head is becoming thicker and he now has eyelashes as well as eyebrows. The three tiny bones of his middle ear are the first bones to harden, which means he is probably capable of hearing, although the auditory centres in his brain, which make sense of sounds received, have not yet developed. The amniotic fluid that surrounds him is an excellent sound conductor and from now on he will hear your stomach rumbling, your heart beating and the sound of your voice, as well as occasional noises from outside the womb. Start singing to him.

The baby now measures approximately 13.5cm (5¼in) and weighs roughly 100g (3½oz).

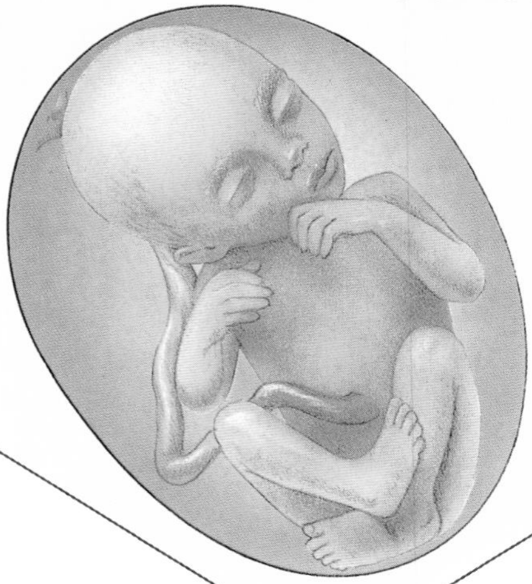

DON'T FORGET Start exercising regularly if you haven't already. Add abdominal and pelvic floor exercises to your programme.

Holidays

You may find that your nesting instinct is very strong during pregnancy and you are happiest staying in your home environment. But if it is your first child you're probably only too aware that this may be your last opportunity for a holiday alone together for a while. But where? And when?

Avoid doing too much travelling during pregnancy as it can be tiring even if you are not driving. Try to plan an enjoyable but essentially restful holiday: relax by a swimming pool or escape to the heart of the countryside. Enjoy the company of your partner.

When is the best time to go away?
First trimester Nausea, vomiting and tiredness may stop you enjoying any travel. If you have to travel, do so in that part of the day when you feel best.
Second trimester This is the best time to go away during pregnancy – especially between Weeks 20 and 27 – although you may still get uncomfortable and restless if you have to sit in cramped conditions on a journey. Walk around as much as you can to keep your circulation going. Your feet are likely to swell on plane journeys, so wear shoes that give.

See Week 17 for Pelvic Floor Exercises

Third trimester It is advisable not to go on any long trips towards the end of pregnancy. Car journeys lasting an hour or so are quite safe, but you may not feel like undertaking more travelling than you have to.

Holiday Do's
- ☐ Talk to your doctor if you want to go away for longer than a month at any stage of your pregnancy.
- ☐ Take your pregnancy notes with you.
- ☐ Check that your insurance covers pregnant women; if not, you may wish to take out extra cover.
- ☐ Check with the doctor that you are allowed to have any vaccinations you may need.
- ☐ Work out a timetable allowing for delays. You won't feel like rushing.
- ☐ Ask the airline if they require a doctor's letter stating that you are fit to fly, especially if you are over thirty weeks pregnant. Most airlines will not let you fly after 36 weeks.
- ☐ Travel by train rather than by car for long distances – it's more comfortable.

Holiday Don't's
- ☐ Don't travel unless absolutely necessary in the first three months if you have had bleeding early in pregnancy or a previous miscarriage.
- ☐ Don't take drugs to prevent sea or air sickness without consulting your doctor.
- ☐ Don't travel far during the last six weeks and stay fairly close to home in the last four.
- ☐ Don't undertake long car journeys (three hours or more) unless accompanied by another driver.
- ☐ Don't eat too much unfamiliar food abroad, especially if highly spiced, and drink bottled, not local water.
- ☐ Don't travel anywhere too hot as you feel hotter naturally as pregnancy progresses.
- ☐ Don't go on a sports holiday. Riding, skiing, climbing and deep-sea diving can all wait.

Week 16

Month: _____   Dates: _____

MON

TUES

WED

THURS

FRI

SAT

SUN

Notes

You If you have already had children you may well feel the first movements of the fetus, called 'quickening', about now. It is a sort of bubbling, fluttering sensation in your stomach.

Baby He is moving vigorously although his movements are rarely felt at this stage in a first pregnancy. However, if this is your second baby you may begin to feel him kick. His head is still quite large in comparison to his body size, but his body is catching up. His face is becoming more human, although his chin is still small and his mouth wide. His eyes are enormous, closed and spaced wide apart.

A fine downy hair (lanugo) appears all over your baby's body and face which is thought to keep him at the right temperature. Most of it will disappear before birth although sometimes a little hair is left which falls out later.

The external genital organs have now developed enough for your baby's sex to be detectable by ultrasound, although your untrained eye will probably not be able to see them.

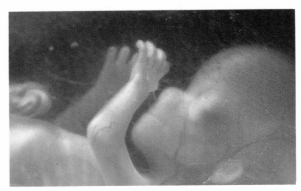

Your baby's skin is developing. It is transparent, but looks red because the blood vessels can be seen through it.

■ **DON'T FORGET** Make a note of the date when you first feel your baby move inside you.

Ultrasound scan

A second visit to the hospital for tests and an ultrasound examination, or scan, takes place around now, usually between Weeks 16 and 18. It may be interesting for your partner to come along to the scan with you.

An ultrasound is the modern equivalent of an X-ray and is at present considered much safer. It works by using sound waves to build up a photographic picture of your baby in the uterus. It can be used at any stage during pregnancy. If you are unsure about having a scan, talk to your doctor about it.

The scan will show you the outline of your baby's head and body on a screen and you will probaby see his backbone wriggling around like a sardine. Ask for the picture to be explained if you can't tell what's what.

What the scan tells you

☐ It determines how old your baby is, which is useful if you are unsure about the date of your last period. If done early in pregnancy this is accurate to within one week.

☐ It measures your baby to check that growth is proceeding normally.

☐ It picks up any visible abnormalities such as brain, head, spine or kidney conditions.

☐ It locates the position of the placenta and its condition.

☐ From around Week 9 an ultrasound scan will be able to detect whether or not you are expecting twins, so be prepared! If you are, you will receive special care and advice during pregnancy.

☐ It detects any growths in you that might make delivery difficult, such as fibroids.

☐ If finds the exact position of your baby and placenta before an amniocentesis is performed (see Week 17).

See Week 17 for Amniocentesis

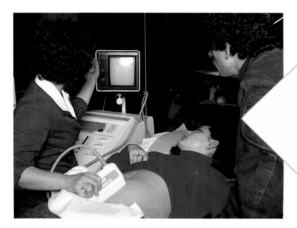

Having a scan

For your ultrasound examination, you lie on a bed and your bare abdomen is smeared with a jelly before the scanning machine is passed over it. The scan is painless (the only requirement being that you have a full bladder) and the results appear immediately on a television screen.

Twins

If you discover that you are expecting twins, you will have to take even greater care of yourself as you will probably get more tired and possibly feel more nauseous. You should take particular care over your diet. You will also have to plan well ahead to organize two lots of clothes and some equipment.

The average duration of a twin pregnancy is 36–38 weeks, so you will need to prepare yourself for labour, and have your hospital case packed earlier. It would be worth reading a book on the subject and contacting a local Twins Club (see Useful Addresses).

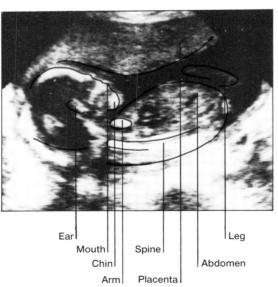

Ear — Mouth — Chin — Arm — Spine — Placenta — Leg — Abdomen

Week 17

Month: Dates:

MON

TUES

WED

THURS

FRI

SAT

SUN

Notes

YOU AND YOUR DEVELOPING BABY

You You may find you are getting some pregnancy problems (see Weeks 11 and 12), such as a blocked nose or an increase in vaginal discharge or that you are sweating more than usual. The sweating is caused by the extra blood circulating in your system and may also make you feel hotter and your cheeks look rosier. All these common symptoms of pregnancy will vanish soon after delivery.

Your uterus is expanding quickly; you should now be able to feel the top of it roughly halfway between your pubic bone and your navel (see Week 20). You will probably have begun to look pregnant too. To reduce the possibility of back pain and discomfort later on, take steps to improve your posture (see Week 31).

Baby He can now hear sounds outside your body, which may make him jump. All his limbs are fully formed, as well as his skin and muscles. The chest muscles are starting to make movements similar to those that will be used in respiration. All his joints are able to move and about now you should begin to feel his movements. Tiny fingernails and toenails are beginning to appear.

Your baby measures approximately 18cm (7⅛in) and now weighs more than the placenta.

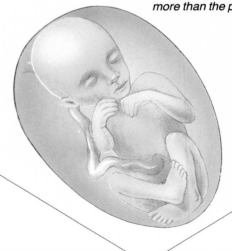

DON'T FORGET Note the date when you first feel your baby moving.

Amniocentesis

Amniocentesis is a test carried out to detect certain abnormalities in the fetus. It has to be done at sixteen to eighteen weeks of pregnancy. A sample of the amniotic fluid which surrounds your baby is drawn out and tested for chromosomal abnormalities, such as Down's syndrome, and congenital abnormalities, such as spina bifida.

An ultrasound scan (see Week 16) is always done before the amniocentesis to check the position of the baby and the placenta so that neither is damaged by the needle. However, there is a small chance of an amniocentesis resulting in a miscarriage, so this test is not done on every expectant mother. Talk to your doctor if you are worried.

You have to wait about four weeks for the result of the test, which can be stressful. If any abnormality is discovered, you will be given the choice of continuing with your pregnancy or terminating it. You may feel there is no point in having an amniocentesis if abortion is against your principles, no matter what is wrong with your child.

Amniocentesis is offered to:

☐ Older women (over 35) for whom there is a higher risk of having a baby with Down's syndrome.

☐ Women who have a family history of Down's syndrome, spina bifida, haemophilia or muscular dystrophy.

☐ Women whose blood sample has shown a raised alpha-fetoprotein level, suggesting a spina bifida baby.

☐ Women who have already had a handicapped child.

See Weeks 21 and 22 for Keeping Fit

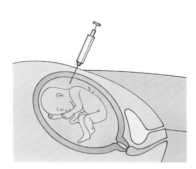

A needle is put through the wall of your abdomen to draw out a sample of amniotic fluid. The fluid is then tested for certain abnormalities.

Pelvic floor exercises
Learning to contract and release your pelvic floor muscles efficiently will help you during labour by making you supple for the birth of your baby. It will also help prevent piles, incontinence and prolapse of your uterus. To see how efficient your pelvic muscles are, the next time you pass urine try to stop in mid-stream, hold for a few seconds and then relax.

Start exercising gradually. You can do pelvic floor exercises lying, sitting or standing. Imagine that your pelvic floor area is a lift going up. Contract it a little until you reach the first floor. Hold it there, then take it to the second floor and so on, until your muscles are fully contracted. Hold them for a count of six. Then release them gradually, floor by floor, until you have reached

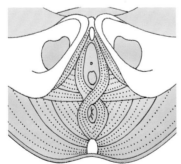

Your pelvic floor muscles are between your legs, forming a figure-8 around your front and back passages. They contract spontaneously during sexual intercourse.

the ground floor. Now push your pelvic floor downwards or away from you, as if you were blowing a candle out with your vagina and pant with your mouth open, slowly and deeply. This is the position your pelvic floor should be in when your baby's head is being born.

Rest and then repeat the above exercise six times, making sure that you are not holding your breath, tightening your shoulders or pulling in your tummy. The rest of your body should always be totally relaxed. If you do the above exercise four times after every visit to the toilet you will soon find you can hold your muscles firmly for a count of nine or ten.

Week 18

Month: Dates:

MON

TUES

WED

THURS

FRI

SAT

SUN

Notes

■ YOU AND YOUR DEVELOPING BABY

You If this is your first pregnancy, it is about now that you will probably feel your baby move for the first time. It's an exciting experience and a day you probably won't ever forget.

If you have flat or 'inverted' (turned in) nipples, it could be a problem in later breast-feeding simply because there is little, if anything, for your baby to latch on to. It may help to massage your nipples several times a day, or you may be offered plastic breast shields to wear for a few hours a day. Most nipple problems, however, will be quickly remedied by a hungry baby.

Baby Your baby is now beginning to test his reflexes. He is kicking and punching with his well-formed arms and legs and possibly sucking his thumb as well. He is also twisting, turning and wriggling about. Inside his developing lungs tiny air sacs, called alveoli, are starting to form.

Your baby measures about 20cm (8in) in length this week and is moving about much of the time.

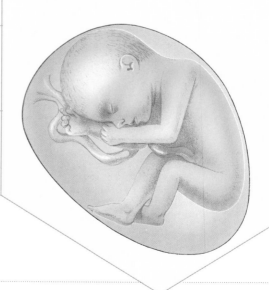

Pregnancy wardrobe

During early pregnancy you may feel you want to attract attention to yourself – to wear bright red and announce to the world that you are expecting a baby. By the end of your pregnancy you will probably have found one or two outfits in which you feel comfortable and which you will want to wear day in, day out.

About now is a good time to go shopping for maternity wear. Earlier than this you may find it depressing seeing those skirts with added flaps and expandable waists: you don't want to imagine the size you will become. Once you've bought some maternity clothes, keep them in the cupboard for as long as you can and wear them only once they have become necessary, otherwise you'll get bored with them too soon – and so will your partner. It makes sense to buy some clothes for this intermediate stage of pregnancy that you can also wear while breast-feeding after the birth, i.e. with front-opening. But make sure you have one or two outfits you feel good in: it's very important for your morale.

Dressing for a winter pregnancy is quite different to dressing for a summer one. In summer you will feel very hot but even in winter you won't feel the cold as much as usual: keep to lightweight natural fibres where possible (worn in layers in winter) and wash them often. Keep clothes loose-fitting – around your armholes as well as your waist.

Draw attention to your face and away from your bump with scarves, bows, collars and sailor's revers. Or draw the eye upwards with bright lipstick, beautiful earrings or a hat.

Dresses Pinafores and smock-style dresses can be worn right through your pregnancy. Don't buy dresses with a tight bodice – you won't want your breasts to be restricted. Dresses with a dropped waist can look good but avoid styles with a seam at the waist: good though they may look around Week 19, they can be unflattering in Week 30.

Shoes Choose shoes that support your feet. Wear the same height of heel throughout your pregnancy: you will find it easiest to stand correctly if your heels are about 2–3cm (1in) high. Avoid high heels: they can throw your weight forward and lead to backache. A long shoe horn will help you to put shoes on in late pregnancy.

Coats Invest in a tent-shaped lightweight raincoat (or a cycling cloak, poncho or shawl), and wear it with layers of clothing. An ordinary coat left unbuttoned can look messy.

Underwear Wear cotton or cotton mix underwear if possible and make sure it is not too tight. Bikini briefs fit best under your bump. Use a lightweight maternity corset if you feel you need support for your stomach. Wear a support bra from about Week 10 of your pregnancy.

Do not wear garters, elastic-top stockings or tight knee socks: they constrict the legs and can cause varicose veins. Wear support tights if you have varicose veins.

Trousers Always buy trousers with an expandable waist. Jogging trousers are comfortable – wear a large shirt, sweatshirt or T-shirt over them to cover your bottom. Dungarees and jumpsuits can be practical but are not always very flattering.

Week 19

Month: Dates:

MON

TUES

WED

THURS

FRI

SAT

SUN

Notes

You You are probably feeling a lot better and happier these days, especially once your baby's kicking has given you tangible proof of his presence. Share your baby's movements with your partner as soon as you can, though he may not be able to feel them as yet.

You will almost certainly have started to look pregnant now. In planning your maternity wardrobe, remember that you have a good few months to go and that the weather will probably not be the same when you are enormous as it is now. You may tire of your pregnancy clothes if you start wearing them too soon.

Baby This week buds for permanent teeth begin forming behind those that have already developed for the milk teeth. By now your child is drinking a considerable quantity of amniotic fluid each day. At the same time, his gut is starting to secrete gastric juices, which will help him absorb the fluid. After absorption the fluid is filtered by his kidneys and excreted back into the amniotic sac.

Your baby now measures approximately 22.5cm (9in) and a first-time mother may feel him move around now.

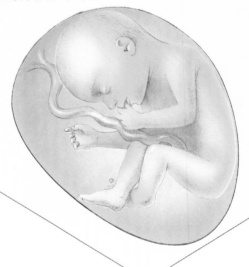

Vitamins and minerals

Ideally, your vitamin and mineral intake will come from food (see Week 3) but some women may need additional supplements. Such cases include:

☐ Women pregnant during adolescence (they are still growing themselves).
☐ Women who are underweight or run-down or who were eating an unbalanced diet when they became pregnant.
☐ Women who were overweight when they became pregnant.
☐ Women on a strict diet, such as vegetarians, vegans and macrobiotics.
☐ Women who are allergic to certain vital foods, such as cow's milk or wheat.
☐ Women who have previously lost a baby from miscarriage or stillbirth.
☐ Women who have had three pregnancies in the last two years.
☐ Women suffering from chronic diseases for which they take continuous medication.
☐ Women who have a multiple pregnancy.
☐ Women who have to work particularly hard or who are under a lot of stress.
☐ Women who smoke, drink or take drugs.
Unless indicated, there is no need to take increased amounts of the following vitamins during pregnancy.

See Week 3 for Healthy Eating

Vitamins

Vitamin A for resistance to infection, relief of allergies or acne, good vision, formation of tooth enamel, hair and fingernails.
☐ Dairy products, oily fish, offal, cooked carrots, apricots, tomatoes and greens.

B Vitamins (1, 2, 3, 5, 6 and 12) for eye and skin problems, nervousness, constipation, lack of energy; milk production, digestion, infection, bleeding gums, development of healthy red blood cells.
☐ Whole grains, wheatgerm (don't overcook), pulses, nuts, offal, pork, egg yolk, brewer's yeast, milk, cheese, mushrooms, potatoes, bananas, green vegetables, oily fish, wholewheat bread, brown rice.

Vitamin C for absorption of iron, strong and healthy tissues, resistance to infection, building a strong placenta and healing fractures and wounds. May be prescribed during pregnancy to help absorb iron.
☐ Citrus fruits, berry fruits, green, red and yellow raw vegetables, potatoes.

Vitamin D for absorption of calcium and phosphorus, and building strong bones.
☐ Found in oily fish, dairy products, liver – and sunlight on the skin.

Vitamin E for improved circulation, varicose veins, piles and hormone production.
☐ Most foods, especially wheatgerm, eggs.

Vitamin K Helps your blood to clot (useful after a difficult delivery).
☐ Green vegetables and alfalfa sprouts.

Folic acid For development of your baby's central nervous system, blood formation, prevention of spina bifida and other malformations. Twice the normal amount is needed during pregnancy and is often prescribed at the same time as iron, after Week 14.
☐ Raw leafy vegetables, walnuts, liver.

Minerals

Calcium Needed for the development of strong bones and teeth in your baby. It also enables your blood to clot and your muscles to work smoothly. You need almost twice as much calcium during pregnancy and breast-feeding, especially in the first four months of pregnancy. Vitamin D is essential for your body to absorb calcium efficiently.
☐ Leafy vegetables, swedes, turnips, cauliflower, fish, oranges, raspberries, blackberries, dairy foods, whole grains, pulses and nuts.

Iron Needed in the formation of haemoglobin for your increased number of red blood cells. Vitamin C helps your body absorb iron. You need about twice as much iron during pregnancy as you do normally. If you are taking antacid medicines for indigestion you may need extra iron (ask your doctor).
☐ Offal, egg yolk, pilchards, sardines, whole grains, pulses, dark green leaf vegetables, raisins, prunes, nuts, dark molasses, brewer's yeast.

Salt Needed in pregnancy because the salt in your blood is diluted by increased body fluids.

43

Week 20

Month: _____   Dates: _____

MON

TUES

WED

THURS

FRI

SAT

SUN

Notes

You Your uterus is beginning to enlarge more rapidly from now on; it presses up against your lungs and pushes your tummy outwards so you begin to look more pregnant. You should be able to feel your uterus just under your navel. Your navel may be starting to flatten or pop out – it will stay that way until after delivery.

Baby Your baby is growing rapidly in both weight and length and now measures approximately 25.5cm (10in) which is roughly half of what the average baby measures at birth. His weight is around 340g (12oz). His growth will soon slow down a little. His muscles are increasing in strength and active movements can now be felt. They may feel like light flutters or like bubbles bursting against your abdomen.

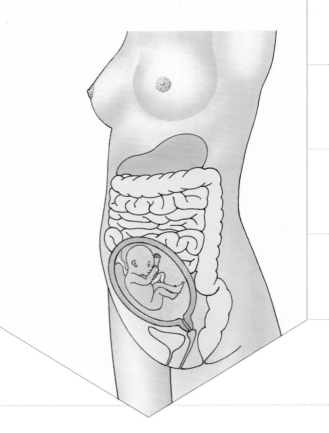

Height of fundus

The fundus is the top of your uterus and its height is a gauge used by your doctor to see how far advanced your pregnancy is. It is normally measured in centimetres from your pubic bone.

In order to accommodate your growing baby your uterus will have to increase its volume about 1,000-fold during pregnancy and, as it does, it will take up the space of other organs. This can lead to some of the problems of later pregnancy, such as breathlessness, constipation, heartburn and frequency of urination.

On average a non-pregnant uterus is roughly the size of a tangerine. It measures approximately 7cm (2¾in) in length, 5cm (2in) in width and is over 2.5cm (1in) thick. By six weeks it is the size of an apple and two weeks later that of an orange. By twelve weeks the uterus is the size of a grapefruit and by Week 14 it will look like a small melon. At full term it can measure as much as 38cm (15in) in length, 25.5cm (10in) in width and 20cm (8in) from front to back. The weight of the uterus itself increases during pregnancy by approximately twenty times, from a pre-pregnant weight of 40g (1½oz) to almost 800g (2lb), at its heaviest, immediately after pregnancy.

With your first child, a phenomenon called 'lightening' may occur after Week 36 which means that your baby drops slightly and engages in your pelvis. Your fundus thus descends a little even though your uterus has not shrunk – this will put pressure on your groin and pelvis. With a second or subsequent baby, this may not happen until the onset of labour.

Although your uterus is expanding throughout your pregnancy, you will probably only notice it after Week 12 when it becomes too large to stay hidden in your pelvis. From then on it enlarges at a regular rate until Week 36 when it reaches to just below your breast-bone. This may make it awkward to breathe and you may feel a jabbing pain in your ribcage.

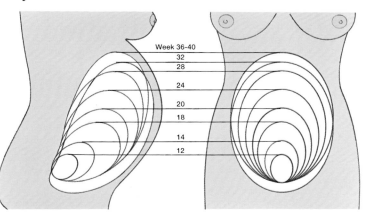

Week 36-40
32
28
24
20
18
14
12

Pre-eclampsia

Pre-eclampsia is a possible condition of later pregnancy involving raised blood pressure and protein in your urine; it rarely occurs before Week 20. It usually develops slowly and there is a risk to both you and your unborn baby if it goes unnoticed. This is one of the reasons why it is important to go for regular antenatal visits at which your blood pressure and urine are tested. If you know what signs to look out for, you can alert your doctor if you notice any or several of them.

It is best to prevent pre-eclampsia, but if it develops and is severe you may have to go to hospital for bedrest, sedation and monitoring of the kidney function and blood pressure. It usually improves under these conditions and will certainly disappear completely once your baby is born.

What the doctor will be looking out for:
☐ swelling of the feet, ankles, face and hands due to fluid retention;
☐ raised blood pressure;
☐ protein in your urine (this is why you take a urine sample to the hospital every visit);
☐ excessive weight gain.

Week 21

Month: Dates:

MON

TUES

WED

THURS

FRI

SAT

SUN

Notes

YOU AND YOUR DEVELOPING BABY

You By the end of this week you should be able to feel the top of your womb about level with your navel. Around now you will probably be starting to feel energetic, healthy and very positive – in short, better than you have ever felt before. You may notice that you are beginning to get a lot done. Remember to rest even if you don't feel like it. You may be feeling constantly hungry as well. During the next ten weeks is when you put on about half of the weight you gain during pregnancy (see Week 25) so watch what you eat. Eat well – but not for two.

Baby Around now your baby's skin becomes opaque. White blood cells are starting to be manufactured, which play an important part in fighting disease and infection. Your child's tongue is now fully developed, and, if female, her internal organs of reproduction – the vagina and the womb – have formed. His legs are now in proportion with the rest of his body and his movements are becoming increasingly sophisticated.

Your baby has been growing steadily and now weighs around 450g (1lb) and measures about 27.5cm (11in) in length.

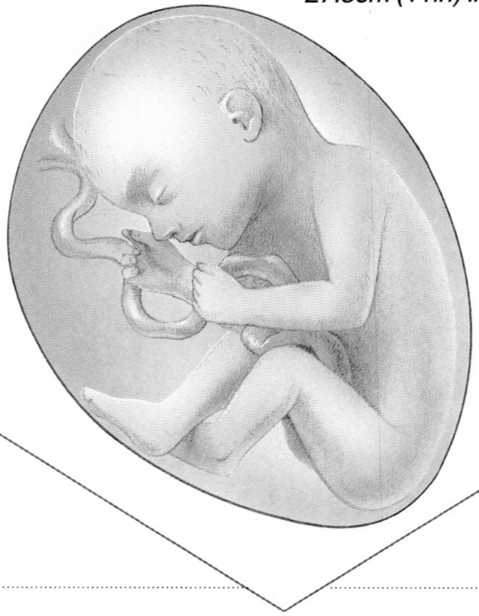

Keeping fit/1

Try and keep active during pregnancy. Not only will it stand you in good stead during your demanding labour but it means you will be less likely to stiffen up as your pregnancy progresses. It will also help you to regain your normal shape more quickly after delivery.

Check with your doctor before exercising during the first three months if you have had a previous miscarriage or are experiencing any complications with this pregnancy. Do all exercises slowly; carry them out rhythmically – never quickly or jerkily – and relax for a minute or two after completing each one.

Never strain yourself and don't exercise until you drop or are in pain. Remember that you are having a baby, not training for the Olympics. Never do sit-ups or raise both legs simultaneously while lying down when you are pregnant. Either can damage your abdominal muscles and strain your back.

Keep breathing at a controlled pace and try to relax the parts of your body which are not being exercised. Arrange pillows where necessary to keep comfortable and always get up from the floor by rolling on to your side and using your arms to push you up. After you have carried out your exercises, lie on your back and rest for a few minutes.

Below are some exercises for you to do gently. Further exercises, to strengthen your back, breast muscles and pelvic muscles, are given in Week 22.

See
Week 17 for
Pelvic Floor
Exercises

See
Week 31 for
Good Posture

Hip stretching
Sit upright on the floor with your back straight (or lean against a wall).
1. With the soles of your feet together, and your heels as near to your body as possible, gently push your knees towards the floor. If this is difficult, push one knee first and then the other.
2. Keeping your legs flat on the floor, move them as far apart as you can. You should feel your groin stretching. ▽

Circulation in legs
1. Lie on your back with a pillow under your knees to prevent back strain. Lift your left leg a little way off the ground and, keeping your knees straight, rotate your left ankle, first clockwise, then anti-clockwise, six times. Repeat with your right ankle.
2. Stand up and, keeping your left foot flat on the ground and your left leg straight, tiptoe on to your right foot. Then, bending your left knee and straightening your right leg, with your right foot now flat on the ground, tiptoe on to your left foot. Do this gentle exercise whenever you have to stand for any length of time.

Tummy muscles (abdominal wall)
1. Lie on your back with your knees bent and your feet flat on the floor. Have a pillow under your head and shoulders. Tighten your tummy muscles so that your abdomen is gently pulled down towards your back. Hold for three seconds, then relax slowly. (This exercise is also good for regaining your figure after birth.)
2. Keeping the small of your back pressed down, slowly stretch both legs until they are straight. Draw one knee back up, and then the other, without lifting the small of your back off the floor. If your back hurts at any point, stop. Otherwise repeat until you can do the exercise ten times. ▽

47

Week 22

Month: _____ Dates: _____

MON

TUES

WED

THURS

FRI

SAT

SUN

Notes

You You will probably notice that your baby is developing a pattern of waking and sleeping and may well be at his most active while you are wanting to sleep. You may sometimes be able to feel him high in your tummy and sometimes low down near your pubis. At this stage his kicks are endearing, and still quite gentle; they will get fiercer!

You may find that you are bringing up small amounts of acid fluid; antacid tablets will help neutralize this. Your gums may bleed more than usual

Baby By the end of the fifth month vernix, a greasy, white, cheesy-looking substance, is beginning to form on your child's skin. Vernix is a mixture of sebum, from the sebaceous glands, and skin cells. It protects your baby's delicate, newly-formed skin from the possible damage of living in liquid for nine months and also against the increasing concentration of urine in the amniotic fluid. The vernix adheres to the lanugo all over the skin. Although most of the vernix will have disappeared before birth, some is left to lubricate your baby's passage along the birth canal during delivery and is one reason why a newborn baby is so slippery and difficult to handle.

Your baby has now grown to about 29cm (11½in) long and weighs about 500g (1lb 2oz).

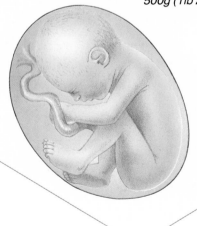

■ **DON'T FORGET** Go and see your dentist if you haven't already.

Keeping fit/2

Below are some more exercises for you to do gently (read Week 21 before starting these). If you can't face even these, do at least go for a daily walk or a swim.

Squatting makes your pelvic joints more flexible and stretches and strengthens thighs and back muscles. It can also relieve back pain.

See Week 31 for Good Posture

Swimming
Start to use the local pool: swimming is wonderful exercise for pregnancy. Even if you can't swim you can exercise by holding on to the side of the pool, with your back to the wall, and cycling in the water, or by facing the side of the pool and swaying gently from side to side.

Squatting
1. Full squats Keeping your back straight, and legs apart, squat down low. Distribute your weight evenly between heels and toes. To further stretch, press elbows against inner thighs.
2. Half squats Hold on to a chair and place your right foot in front of your left. Point your right knee slightly out and slowly bend both knees. Keep your bottom tucked in and back straight. Stand up slowly, then repeat with the other leg in front.

Back strengthening
1. Pelvic rock Lie on your back with your feet together, flat on the floor, and knees slightly bent. Place a hand under the hollow of your back. Using your stomach muscles, press your spine against the floor until your back is flat. Relax and repeat.
2. The cat Get on all fours with your hands and knees apart. Arch your back gently and push your head down so you feel a stretch from neck to tail. Now raise your head as you relax your back to its normal position. Repeat once.

Breast muscles
Sit cross-legged on the floor with your back straight. Bend your arms and grip your left wrist with your right hand and vice versa. Breathe in and blow out once. Now breathe in, hold your breath and push your shoulders and ribcage down. Tip your chin gently on to your chest and push your arm muscles towards your elbows ten times. Then raise your head and blow out slowly. Repeat once. If you find you can't hold your breath for so long, build up to it slowly.

Week 23

Month: *Dates:*

MON

TUES

WED

THURS

FRI

SAT

SUN

Notes

You You may have already noticed a painless, though uncomfortable, hardening of your stomach which occurs roughly every twenty minutes and lasts for twenty seconds. You may have thought it was your baby's foot or bottom pushing your tummy, but this is a 'Braxton Hicks' uterine contraction; they occur all the way through pregnancy, although they are not usually noticeable before this stage. They help your uterus grow and ensure a good circulation of blood through your uterine vessels.

You may also sometimes get a stitch-like pain down the side of your tummy, which is your uterine muscle stretching. Have a rest and the pain will go.

Baby Your baby is now moving vigorously, often in response to touch and sound. A loud noise nearby may make him jump and kick. He is also swallowing small amounts of amniotic fluid and passing tiny amounts of urine back into it. Sometimes he may get hiccups and you can feel the jerk of each hiccup.

His heartbeat can now be heard through a stethoscope. Your partner may even be able to hear it by putting his ear to your tummy, but he has to find the right place and the room has to be quiet.

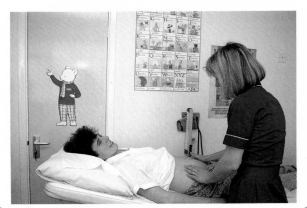

The midwife may have to move the baby into a position where his heartbeat can be heard.

The father's role

Your partner is no doubt as pleased as you are about your pregnancy and the future baby. He will also be concerned, although his anxieties may well be different from yours. He may worry about how your relationship will change, about how his life will be disrupted and about whether he is going to be able to support you both financially (especially if you are giving up work). It may also be difficult at first for him to realize that a baby is really there; it can feel strange being so closely involved and yet in a sense so removed.

Include him as much as possible, and make him feel proud – after all, it is his baby

too. Let him feel the baby kicking, invite him along to hospital appointments, antenatal classes and, of course, the birth – but don't be upset if he feels he doesn't want to come. If he doesn't attend, let him know all you've been told at the hospital or at classes. But try not to become a pregnancy bore unless you feel he is really interested. If it is your first child, try and do as much together now as you can, whether it's reading the papers in bed in the morning, going to the cinema regularly or going on holiday.

Explain to your partner how you are feeling, because your emotions will be changing a lot more than usual. Make sure you apologize if you find yourself snapping at him. Try and get him to help out if you are

feeling sick or too tired to do anything – especially during the first and the last three months. If you have other children, he can play a very important part in your pregnancy (see Week 14).

Your partner may feel jealous both of the coming child and of your ability to nurture new life within you. He may also dislike being the supporting actor rather than the star and may feel he is only peripherally helpful. Partners need both physical and mental reassurance. Even if you don't feel like sex, cuddle and caress him, and try not to let the ten pillows that surround your body in bed every night get in between you too much! Try and talk to your partner about his emotions and worries, even if you feel more like concentrating on yourself.

See Week 38 for Fathers in Labour

See Weeks 6 and 24 for Sex during Pregnancy

To fathers
Be positive and appreciative: always let your partner know she is doing her best. Try to be sympathetic and supportive – always show her you love her and help her where you can. If at times you feel left out, rest assured that what you are sharing will bond the two of you closer together all your lives. Read all you can about pregnancy and childbirth, and prepare yourself for adjustments afterwards.

Practical checklist for fathers
- [ ] Do you know the quickest route to the hospital, the correct entrance and where you can park?
- [ ] Have you visited the hospital beforehand to see where the delivery rooms, canteen and wards are?
- [ ] Have you put a rug and some cushions in the car?
- [ ] Do you know what the signs of labour are? (See Week 37)
- [ ] Have you discussed what your partner feels about pain relief? (See Week 35)
- [ ] If you want to attend the birth, are you as knowledgeable about it as your partner?
- [ ] Are the relevant phone numbers displayed by the phone? (See Week 37)

Week 24

Month: _____ Dates: _____

MON

TUES

WED

THURS

FRI

SAT

SUN

Notes

YOU AND YOUR DEVELOPING BABY

You You may begin to put on weight fairly rapidly about now and your feet will probably start to feel the strain. Check that your shoes are comfortable and give you enough support; go barefoot at home if you feel like it. Rest with your feet up – preferably above your heart – whenever possible.

If you are finding your job more and more exhausting try to arrange to leave work, or to work part-time, from early in the third trimester (from Week 28 on) if your employer agrees.

Baby Your baby is still rather thin and his skin quite wrinkled because he has not yet laid down deposits of fat, but he is growing lengthwise. His arms and legs now have a normal amount of muscle and they are moving vigorously. Creases are appearing on his palms and fingertips.

If he was delivered this week his vital organs are sufficiently developed for him to be able to survive for a short time, but his lungs are not quite mature enough for him to be able to live for long outside your uterus.

Your baby's hands are active at this time. This muscular coordination is sufficiently developed for him to suck his thumb!

Problems of later pregnancy

Some minor problems, or discomforts, start in early pregnancy and continue until the last few months (see Weeks 11 and 12). Others only begin towards, or during, the final trimester. You may of course experience few, or none, of them.

Backache See Week 31
Breathlessness From about Week 30 you might find

Discomfort in bed
This could be due to indigestion or heartburn, or to pressure from your enlarged uterus. If your mattress is not firm, place a board under it. Distribute pillows under different parts of your body until you get comfortable. Lying on your right side may be most comfortable (see Week 31).

---

breathing difficult, due to pressure on your diaphragm from your growing uterus. It will become easier once your baby's head has engaged. Remember to sit up or stand as straight as possible, and prop a few pillows under your head and shoulders in bed. If you have chest pain or swelling, consult your doctor.
Incontinence You may leak a little urine when you cough, laugh or bend down. This could be due to your enlarged uterus pressing on your bladder, or to weak pelvic floor muscles (see Week 17). Empty your bladder often and avoid lifting anything heavy; exercise your pelvic floor.

Indigestion and heartburn
Some of the foods you normally enjoy may give you indigestion. If you can work out what they are, avoid them. Eat smaller meals and sit up straight when eating to take the pressure off your stomach.

Heartburn is a burning pain in the lower part of your chest, throat, back of your mouth or stomach, often accompanied by the regurgitation of sour fluid. It is caused by the relaxation of a stomach valve, allowing acid to pass into the tube.

Sleep with your shoulders well propped up, or even with telephone directories under the head end of your bed. A glass of milk, or spring or soda water, before sleeping may help. Don't sit slumped in a chair and try not to bend down, putting your head below your chest; avoid rich, fried or spicy foods; and wear clothes that are loose at the waist. If the problem gets serious, see your doctor.
Nausea Nausea towards the end of pregnancy may be due to the pressure of your uterus on your stomach. Eat small, frequent meals. (See Week 7)
Pelvic discomfort You may develop pain around your pubic area, or in your groin and down the inside of your thighs. This could be caused by your baby's head pressing on nerves, or by your pelvic joints softening in preparation for labour. Don't stand or sit for long periods and avoid violent exercise. Rest frequently and take the occasional Paracetamol tablet if the pain gets too uncomfortable.
'Pins and needles' This is due to the increase in body fluid exerting pressure on your

nerves and tendons. Hold your hands above your head and wriggle your fingers.
Rib pain After about Week 30, when the top of the uterus is high, you may feel a pain just below your breasts. You will feel most comfortable sitting on a straight chair or lying down flat. Stretch upwards to lift your ribcage off your uterus.
Swelling of legs, ankles, fingers (oedema) Oedema is an increase in fluid retention in your body, especially in the lower limbs. This is due to the pressure of the uterus on the vessels that return blood from the lower parts of your body to the heart. You may notice your shoes feeling tight, your ankles becoming wrinkled and your rings not fitting. Mention this to your doctor in case it is a sign of pre-eclampsia (see Week 20). Avoid standing, and rest on your bed for an hour or two a day, with your feet raised above your heart. It may help to wear maternity support tights. Avoid garters or tight socks or shoes.

Sex in later pregnancy
The classic missionary position (with the man on top) is uncomfortable in the later stages. But this is no reason to give up sex. Try 'the spoons' position, both facing the same way – you lying on your side with your partner close behind you. Or you can kneel or crouch so your partner can enter you from behind. Or find ways other than penetration to have sex.

See Week 6 for Your Relationship

See Weeks 11 and 12 for Common Problems

Week 25

MON

TUES

WED

THURS

FRI

SAT

SUN

Notes

YOU AND YOUR DEVELOPING BABY

You Around now is the best time in pregnancy for many women. Make the most of it. You may find that you are looking flushed and rosy-cheeked with the increase in blood circulation underneath your skin. You should also be feeling happy and contented; if you are not, try and talk about it to your partner, friends and your doctor.

The minus side is that you may be experiencing some of the problems of pregnancy, such as backache, cramp and a desire to urinate more often. Your heart and lungs are now doing fifty per cent more work than usual and you will find that you are sweating more because of your raised body fluid levels.

Baby Your baby's bone centres are beginning to harden. From now on he is growing slowly and steadily, his body growing at a faster pace to catch up with the size of his head. He will be fattening out as well, so that his eyes seem less hollow in his head. During the last seven days he will have grown approximately 1cm (just under ½in) and gained about 85g (just over 3oz) in weight.

Growing at a steady pace, your baby now measures about 35cm (1ft 2in) and weighs around 850g (1lb 14oz).

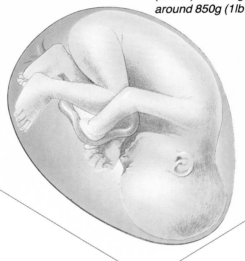

Weight gain in pregnancy

At one stage it was thought that pregnant women should 'eat for two'. Then opinions changed and women were led to believe that they should try not to gain weight during pregnancy as it would stay with them forever. Today, studies show that underweight women are probably at greater risk of bearing low-birthweight babies and that a steady weight gain is desirable.

You will be weighed each time you go to the clinic, partly to show that your baby is growing normally and partly to check on your own health: a sudden change up or down in weight could signify problems. If you are putting on too much weight it could indicate a condition of pre-eclampsia (see Week 20). Dieting and cutting down on fluids will not help, so continue to eat well.

The diagram below shows how your weight gain is made up. However much weight you put on during pregnancy, you will gain roughly a quarter of the total between Weeks 12 and 20, half between Weeks 20 and 30 and the last quarter between Weeks 30 and 38. If you find your weight shooting up at the end, this is probably due to water retention, so don't worry. You will lose it all after your baby is born, although it follows that the less weight you put on, the easier this will be lost.

See Week 3 for Healthy Eating

See Week 19 for Vitamins and Minerals

Most women gain about 13.5kg (30lb) altogether during pregnancy and find that they are 3–6kg (7–14lb) heavier after giving birth than before they became pregnant. The amount varies between individuals and in one woman from one pregnancy to the next.

One indication of how much superfluous fat you will be left with after the birth is to measure your upper thighs each week. Their circumference should stay the same throughout most of your pregnancy, as this is your own body fat, although towards the end of your pregnancy fluid retention may increase this measurement.

Remember that individual women gain weight at different rates. If you are worried about your weight, discuss it with your doctor; do not start slimming during pregnancy. You can do more harm to yourself and your baby by eating too little of the foods you need than by eating too much.

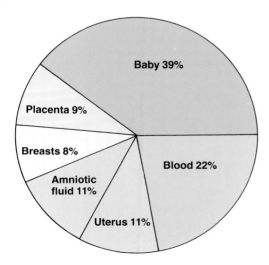

Pregnancy weight gain chart

Week 26

Month: Dates:

MON

TUES

WED

THURS

FRI

SAT

SUN

Notes

YOU AND YOUR DEVELOPING BABY

You Take advantage of your surplus energy and any spare time to start preparing for your child's arrival. If you think you're busy now, you'll certainly be busier later on! Get organized: make lists of anything you need to do around your home and any clothes and other equipment you need to buy.

If you haven't already, start to use the local swimming pool, go for a daily walk or do a regular programme of exercises.

Baby The branches of your baby's lungs (the bronchi) are now developing, but his lungs will not be fully formed until after he is born. His head is now in better proportion to his body and will start growing fast now. Fat stores are beginning to accumulate.

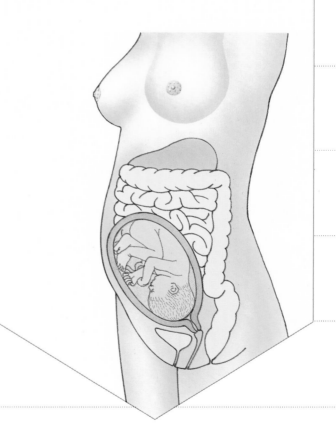

Preparing for baby

It is not essential that your baby has a room of his own: he can equally well share with older siblings or with you. If he's to share your bedroom it is a good idea to keep him in a separate corner so you will have some privacy. Put a well-shaded lamp in the baby's section so as not to wake your partner (unless he wants to help) when you have to change and feed your child in the night.

If he can have his own room, it's nice to make it bright and colourful and appealing for a child, but there is no need to spend a lot of money on baby equipment or on totally redecorating a room that has just been done. Your child will be happiest sleeping and playing in a room in which he can relax and enjoy himself – and that won't happen if you are worried about him ruining the decor. Remember that he will grow quickly and his requirements will constantly be changing. Whether you are preparing the baby's room from scratch or furnishing and adapting a room, there are several considerations to bear in mind.

Floors If you haven't yet laid a carpet, consider using non-slip lino or vinyl (easy to clean), or else cork or carpet tiles so that you can replace the odd one rather than the whole carpet. Use non-slip polish on wooden floors and make sure there are no splinters. Small mats or rugs can be slippery, so avoid them or use a non-slip backing.

Furniture Furniture should be sufficiently heavy that it can't be pulled over. Paint any baby furniture that you inherit, such as cot or crib, with non-toxic paint (i.e. not lead-based) for safety. Bring in a low, comfortable chair (preferably without arms) with a straight back for feeding and put a small table or storage box at the side.

You will need drawer space for clothes and some storage space for nappies. Provided a chest of drawers is the right height, you could use the top of it as a changing place.

Heating It is important that your baby's room is kept warm by day and night in cold weather. Buy a heater with a thermostat or put a thermostat-control on the radiator, and try to keep a constant temperature of about 18°C (65°F) for the first few weeks.

Free-standing heaters must be either blower or convector-types. Coal, electric bar or gas fires must be screened by a fixed guard with a small mesh. Rooms heated by gas and oil heaters must be properly ventilated and heaters regularly serviced. Install a humidifier if the air gets too dry.

Lamps Overhead lighting is preferable: table lamps can be knocked over and electric wires tripped over. Cover sockets with special childproof covers. A dimmer switch or night-light allows ·you to check your baby without waking him up.

Walls Painted walls are easier to clean. Wallpaper should be washable and preferably have a pattern that doesn't show every fingerprint.

Windows Make sure windows (and doors) are draughtproof or that your baby does not sleep too close to them. Windows should be fixed so that they cannot be opened far enough for him to fall out. Guard low windows with close-spaced vertical bars (removable in case of fire). Use a thick material for curtains or line them well to make sure they keep the light out. You can buy a special rubber-backed 'blackout' lining material (which is in fact white).

In this nursery, useful storage – shelves, chest of drawers and toy box – combine with colourful accessories – frieze and cot mobile – to make an attractive and practical room.

See Weeks 27 and 28 for Shopping for Equipment

See Week 32 for Getting Ready

See Week 33 for Shopping for Layette

Week 27

Month: Dates:

MON

TUES

WED

THURS

FRI

SAT

SUN

Notes

■ YOU AND YOUR DEVELOPING BABY

You You are probably beginning to put on weight at a steady rate and may be aware that you are starting to get more tired. As you come to the end of your middle trimester, you may begin to experience a few of the minor problems commonly associated with later pregnancy (see Week 24).

You may notice quite regular Braxton Hicks contractions now, especially when walking. Try wearing a lightweight maternity corset if you feel it would help. Keep exercising. You should now be able to feel the top of your uterus about halfway between your navel and your breast bone.

Baby Around this week the membranes which formed your baby's eyelids part, and his eyelids open for the first time. His eyes are almost always blue or dark blue at this stage as the eye colouring is not fully developed until a few months after birth. Occasionally, however, a baby's eyes turn brown within only a few hours of him being born.

Your baby now weighs about 900g (2lb) and measures around 36cm (1ft 2in).

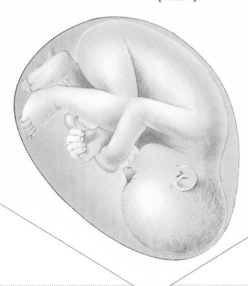

Shopping for equipment/1

It is a good idea to shop for equipment, and possibly baby clothes too, at this stage, while you still have the energy. You will probably feel too tired and uncomfortable for shopping in the later stages of pregnancy – and you will have no time at all once the baby is born! If you feel it is 'tempting fate' to fill the house with baby things before he is even born, most stores will let you order major pieces of equipment now, provided you leave a deposit, and will deliver them to your home after the birth. Or buy from shops that will let you return unused goods – and keep all your receipts.

If this is your first baby it can be difficult to know exactly what you will need and the choice can be baffling. The suggestions below and in Week 28 will help you to make decisions. If this is your second or subsequent child, you probably already have most of the furniture and equipment you'll need. If you're buying new equipment, always make sure that it complies with British Standards Institution safety regulations.

Below is a list of major items of sleep equipment you might buy and the points to bear in mind when choosing them.

Cot You don't need a full-size cot at first but something smaller, such as a carrycot, crib, Moses basket or pram.

If you borrow or inherit a used cot, check that the paint or varnish is non-toxic and that there are not splinters or sharp bits anywhere. Check also that the gap between bars conforms with British Safety Standards. In choosing a new one, see that it's sturdy enough and that the sides are high enough to prevent a child climbing out. Choose one with a drop side or you'll have to stoop low to lift your baby in and out, but check that it has a safety catch to prevent him letting down the sides himself when he is older. Some cots convert into a bed later.

Cot mattress This needs to be firm and is best covered with plastic. It should fit the cot without leaving a space round the edges.

Bedding You will need at least three bottom sheets. Fitted towelling or flannelette sheets are cosy though they take longer to dry. Your baby won't use top sheets for the first few weeks as he will be wrapped in a shawl or light blanket. After that three non-fitted flannelette sheets will be enough. He must not use a pillow for at least the first year, but he will need blankets or a blanket and quilt. Several light layers (preferably cotton cellular blankets) are warmer and more comfortable than one heavy one; avoid fringes which your baby may suck.

Baby alarm This will let you hear the baby crying if you live in a large or noisy house. You can get one that plugs into your main electrical circuit so you can take it easily from room to room.

See Week 28 for Shopping for Equipment/2

See Week 33 for Shopping for Layette

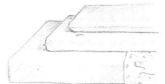

◁ *A useful feature in some cots is an adjustable height mattress.*

A Moses basket makes a cosy first bed. ▷

You can get spring interior cot mattresses (bottom) or ones made of foam with or without air vents. ▷

Week 28

Month: Dates:

MON

TUES

WED

THURS

FRI

SAT

SUN

Notes

You Week 28 is the first week of your third and last trimester, which often seems the longest. Some of the minor problems of pregnancy, such as indigestion and cramp, may have become a part of life but be assured they will disappear after the birth. Get as much rest and sleep as possible and keep up your calcium intake by eating more milk, cheese or yoghurt.

Baby At 28 weeks your baby is considered legally 'viable', which means he is thought capable of sustaining separate and independent life if born. It also means that if he is delivered he must be registered. His lungs are reaching maturity and although he might have breathing problems and difficulty keeping himself warm if born, with modern special care facilities he has a chance of survival.

By now your baby is large enough for his position in your uterus to be assessed during an abdominal examination. He may be in the usual head downwards position, or in a breech position (see Understanding your Hospital Notes, page 88).

Your baby now measures approximately 37cm (1ft 2½in) and weighs roughly 1kg (2lb 3oz).

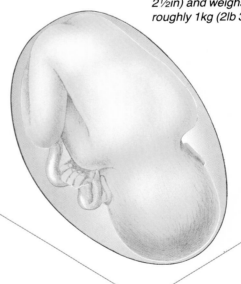

Shopping for equipment/2

Major items of equipment for transporting and bathing your baby are assessed below.

Pram Think carefully about this: you may find your needs are more suited to a carrycot on wheels (see below). When choosing a pram, check that it is light enough for you to push easily, that the handles are at a comfortable height and that the brakes can be operated without letting go of the handle. Make sure the hood goes up and down easily, that the wheels run smoothly (large wheels may be easier to push), that the mattress is firm and that a shopping tray can be fitted without interfering with the brakes. Make sure there are anchor points for a safety harness. Check that you'll be able to get it through your front door. With a second-hand pram, make sure the tyres are not worn and that there are no nuts loose or missing.

Pram harness Buy one that is strong and washable and easy to fasten and unfasten.

Pram net This will keep off insects.

Pushchair Newborn babies shouldn't travel in upright or even semi-upright pushchairs as their back muscles are not strong enough to support them sitting up. Wait until your baby has grown out of the carrycot or pram before buying a pushchair, or buy one that will let him lie flat or that will take a carrycot clipped to the main frame.

The most useful pushchair has a seat that can be altered into several positions, and some can even face forwards or backwards. Make sure the back is firm enough to give support. Are there built-in safety straps, or anchor points for your pram harness? Check that it's light enough to carry easily and see how simple it is to fold with one hand – imagine holding a baby in the other. See whether a shopping tray can be fitted without interfering with the brakes, and whether a waterproof cover and sun canopy can be fitted. Make sure that it will fit easily into your car, if you have one.

Baby carrier or sling Your baby will enjoy being held close to you and it leaves your hands free. Check that it has adjustable straps and a padded head support, preferably detachable for later.

Carrycot on wheels This may suit you better than a pram if you are using the carrycot as your baby's bed, or taking it in the car. Check that it will fit into your car; restraints are needed to strap it to the back seat. Make sure the handles are strong and well balanced and that the cot is light enough to carry. You may not need wheels if you have a pram as well. Check that the transporter is easily collapsible.

Bath Look for easy drainage, a soap dish at one end and one sloping end so that the baby can stretch out. Make sure the stand, if it has one, is absolutely steady.

Changing mat Buy a plastic-covered one with raised sides.

See Week 27 for Shopping for Equipment/1

See Week 33 for Shopping for Layette

Equipment for transporting baby

An all-in-one pushchair with carrycot.

A multi-position pushchair.

A carrycot and transporter.

A baby carrier is useful early on.

Week 29

Month: *Dates:*

MON

TUES

WED

THURS

FRI

SAT

SUN

Notes

You By now you will probably be able to tell your baby's bottom from his knee. In the bath you may be able to watch him move from one side of your abdomen to another. His hand movements are softer than his rather jerky knee and foot movements.

If you haven't already done so, go for a swim. You will enjoy feeling much lighter than you do normally. You may start needing to sit down often and you probably won't feel like running around. Start delegating some chores to your partner.

Baby Your baby has filled almost all the space in your uterus and his head is now more or less in proportion with his body. Although he may still be lying with his head up, within a few weeks he should have turned upside down and will then appear to fit more comfortably. He is growing at a weekly rate of just under 1cm (³⁄₈in) and now measures around 38cm (1ft 3in).

Your baby is gaining about 200g (7oz) a week and now weighs about 1.02kg (2lb 4oz).

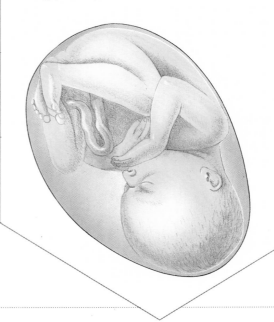

Learning relaxation

Relaxing is all about releasing the tension in your body and in your mind. Being able to relax both physically and mentally will help you during labour to counteract the natural response to pain, which is to tense your muscles and hold your breath. Imagine how you react to a stressful situation, such as a traffic jam, with shoulders hunched, teeth gritted and hands clenched. Once you can relax both during and between contractions, you will be able to work *with* them. Learning to release tension also involves correct breathing (see Week 34). If you find it difficult to relax, practise the exercises below every day.

Antenatal classes
Antenatal classes are designed to help you keep fit during your pregnancy and to prepare both you and your partner for the birth. Most of them cover 'parentcraft' – the basic aspects of looking after a baby. The weekly classes usually start eight to ten weeks before your baby is due.

Antenatal classes will certainly be run by your hospital, and there may be more local classes organized by your doctor or the health centre. The National Childbirth Trust hold their own classes, for which there is a charge: to join, find out who your local organizer is. Book in early for all classes, since numbers are often restricted.

Some classes are in the evening but even the daytime classes offer a 'fathers' evening'. If your hospital is nearby it may be a good idea to go to their classes as you then become familiar with it. The advantage of going to classes run by the local health centre or doctor's surgery is that you will meet local expectant mothers and the midwives and health visitors who will be looking after you and your baby.

See Week 34 for Breathing for Labour

Physical relaxation
Start by getting comfortable. Either sit or lie but arrange pillows around you so that every bit of your body is supported. Begin with your toes. First tense up all of the muscles in your toes and then relax them, letting them go so that they are all floppy. Then tense your feet – and let go.

Carry on up your body: your calves, thighs, buttocks, stomach and so on, right up to your face, tensing and then relaxing every single part. This should take about five minutes. Then do it again, this time beginning from the top. Carry on until your whole body is as floppy as a rag doll.

Mental relaxation
Get comfortable and clear your mind of anything that's making you nervous. Then concentrate on your breathing: breathe in deeply, hold your breath for a count of five seconds, and then breathe out slowly. As you do so, make sure all your muscles are relaxed – drop your shoulders and jaw, and unclench your hands – and continue to breathe deeply.

Then let your imagination flow. Picture yourself on a beach in the sun under a blue sky, hearing the gentle noise of the waves beside you, or imagine you are floating up to the clouds. Choose whatever image appeals to you.

Relaxing with your partner
Your partner can help you to relax. He must firmly massage the part of your body that is tense so that his hands draw the tension out of you. If you have a headache, for example, let your partner stand behind you and, with two fingers, firmly press each side of your head, against your temples. As he gradually lessens the pressure, your tension will ease away. He can do the same with your shoulders, only this time using the whole of his hands rather than just his fingers. The regular rhythm of gentle stroking will help you to relax generally; this can be useful in the early stages of labour.

63

Week 30

Month: Dates:

MON

TUES

WED

THURS

FRI

SAT

SUN

Notes

YOU AND YOUR DEVELOPING BABY

You During the next ten weeks your baby will be gaining about 200g (7oz) a week and you will be gaining almost twice as much. From now on you will become much larger, slower and clumsier. You may feel as if all your internal organs are being squeezed out and put under pressure from your enlarging uterus.
Baby Your baby is probably lying in a curled-up position with his knees bent, his arms and legs crossed and his chin resting on his chest. He now begins to move less and to settle, and within the next two weeks will have turned upside down if he has not already done so. Most babies adopt a head downwards position so that they can be born head first. If your baby is one of the four per cent who has his bottom downwards ('breech' presentation) your doctor will probably try and turn him round later on.

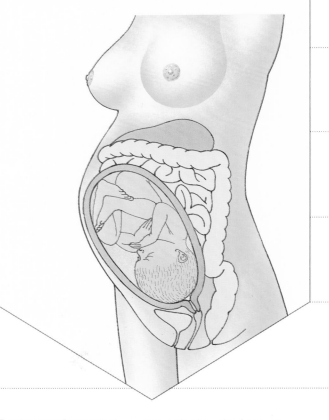

DON'T FORGET If you haven't already done so, stop smoking now. Your baby needs oxygen to enable him to grow and smoking reduces the amount he will get.

Thinking about feeding

If this is your first baby you may find it hard to know how you will want to feed him. You don't have to decide now, but if you are at all uncertain it is best to start with breast-feeding, as you can always change to bottle-feeding later. It is much more difficult to breast-feed when you have started with bottle-feeding.

Breast-feeding

Breast-feeding is certainly best for the health of your baby. Breast milk contains all the nourishment he needs. It is the right temperature and right consistency and, being easily digested, is less likely to cause diarrhoea, constipation or stomach upsets. Breast milk provides antibodies which help to protect your baby against coughs, colds and chest infections; it also helps prevent allergies, such as eczema and asthma.

Breast-feeding is easier and cheaper than bottle-feeding. It is also convenient – your milk is always available, even when travelling. Breast-fed babies are unlikely to get fat. They take as much milk as they need.

Breast-feeding can be emotionally satisfying for the mother. It may also help you regain your figure, due partly to the calories burned up and also because the hormones involved in breast-feeding cause 'afterpains' which help your uterus to contract back to its pre-pregnancy size and position.

Some mothers find that breast-feeding can be uncomfortable or even painful at first, but this soon settles down. If you feel that breast-feeding could become a tie, remember that you can express your milk for your baby to have in a bottle. It is important to sleep and eat well while feeding and you may have to avoid eating certain foods such as strawberries or spicy things.

The only 'equipment' you will need for breast-feeding are three nursing bras (you may want to wear them at night too). They should be adjustable (the size of your breasts will change) and easy to open at the front with one hand. You will also need disposable breast pads to soak up leaking milk, or you could use muslin squares.

Bottle-feeding

If you do decide to bottle-feed, there is no need to feel guilty. The most important thing in feeding is to be relaxed and hold your baby close. Some women feel that bottle-feeding will leave them freer to carry on their own life and of course it is an experience that can be shared by the father. With bottle-feeding you can see exactly how much milk your baby has taken, and some mothers find this reassuring.

You may, however, find all the sterilizing and preparation required for bottle-feeding hard work, and very time-consuming, at first. There is also a danger of your baby becoming overweight, since it is easy to over-feed with bottle formulas.

Bottle-feeding is more expensive than breast-feeding. Besides buying the powdered formula milk, you also need a lot of equipment (see below). In addition to the six bottles and teats, you should have some form of sterilizing unit or must boil equipment carefully every day.

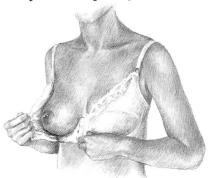

◁ *Nursing bras should be front-opening and adjustable; they should also give your breasts some support.*

In the interests of your baby's health, all bottle-feeding equipment must be sterilized before use. The powdered formula milk has to be measured and made up accurately. ▷

Week 31

MON

TUES

WED

THURS

FRI

SAT

SUN

Notes

YOU AND YOUR DEVELOPING BABY

You You are probably beginning to feel breathless when you overdo things, which may make you become impatient for the birth. Or, you may find yourself becoming completely absorbed with your body and your baby's movements. It can be quite a dilemma. Just take care if you do find yourself withdrawing from the world around you. Make sure you don't let your partner feel left out.

If your breasts are becoming heavy, begin wearing a well-fitting bra at night as well as during the day from now on. Good support will make them feel more comfortable.

Baby As your baby grows plumper, his skin fills out and becomes smoother. Both the vernix and the lanugo begin to disappear.

Around this week the air sacs in his lungs become lined with a layer of cells which produce a liquid called surfactant. This will prevent the air sacs from collapsing when your baby begins to breathe after birth.

This week your baby measures around 39cm (1ft 3½ in) and weighs about 1.4kg (3lb 2oz).

DON'T FORGET Never stand up when you can sit, and never sit when you can lie down.

Good posture

Backache can occur at any time during pregnancy, though the greatest risk is now. If your stomach muscles are not strong enough to carry your extra weight, your back muscles are forced to work to support your spine. This puts strain on them. It will help to learn, or relearn, how to stand, sit and lie properly.

When standing
Always stand as straight as possible and don't lean backwards. Improve your posture by wearing low (or flat) heels, tucking your buttocks in, keeping your shoulders dropped and carrying yourself as if you want the top of your head to touch the ceiling. Avoid stooping; instead kneel, sit or squat to do the ironing, peel potatoes, clean the bath etc.

When sitting
Sit well back in a chair and support your back by putting a rolled-up towel or small cushion in the hollow of your spine. Try sitting cross-legged when you can.

When lying down
Use a firm mattress and lie flat on your back or on your side. Support your body with pillows wherever they are needed – if lying on your side, try placing them under your head and upper arm; under your stomach; under your top knee and under your hips. To ease upper backache, lie flat on your back with pillows under your head and knees (provided you are comfortable lying on your back).

To get up
To avoid straining your back and abdominal muscles, roll on to your side first and push yourself up using your arm muscles.

Lifting and carrying
Avoid lifting anything heavy if you can. If you have to pick something up, squat down keeping your back straight.

If you need to carry heavy items, keep them close to your body. Distribute the weight evenly: put shopping in two bags of equal weight rather than a single heavy one.

Low backache
To relieve your spine of your baby's weight, get on all fours as often as possible. Do the cat exercise (see Week 22) whenever you can and, if you feel like it, scrub the kitchen floor daily!

See
Week 24 for
Discomfort
in Bed

Remember to keep your back straight whenever you sit cross-legged. ▷

Squat down using your leg muscles to pick things up – it prevents straining your back. ▷

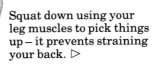

◁ Get up from a lying position by first rolling on to your side then pushing yourself up on to your elbow.

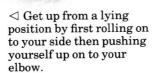

Week 32

Month: Dates:

MON

TUES

WED

THURS

FRI

SAT

SUN

Notes

▪ YOU AND YOUR DEVELOPING BABY

You As your uterus rises and your baby and uterus push up under your diaphragm, the bottom edge of your ribcage may become quite sore. You may experience a loss of libido (sexual desire) during the next few weeks; on the other hand, many women find sex exciting around this time of pregnancy.

Baby Your child is now perfectly formed, although still relatively thin, and his proportions are much as you would expect them to be at birth. If he were born now he would have a very good chance of survival, because his lungs are almost developed. He would however need to be placed in an incubator as not enough insulating fat reserves have yet been deposited beneath his skin.

His movements are now very vigorous and may even be quite uncomfortable, especially if his feet get caught under your ribs; sitting up straight will help counteract this. You will probably be aware of him getting hiccups whenever he swallows some amniotic fluid. Each week he will have less and less room to move about and the 'lie', the position he has taken up in the womb, will be checked to make sure he is lying head downwards ready for birth. If not, your doctor will decide whether to try and turn the baby, or if special delivery techniques will be needed.

Your baby now weighs about 1.6kg (3lb 10oz) and measures 40.5cm (just over 1ft 4in).

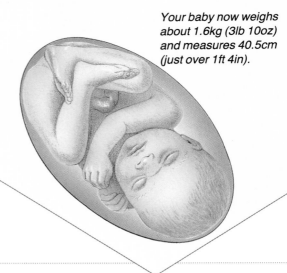

▪ **DON'T FORGET** Begin your antenatal classes now if you haven't already.

Getting ready

that some time in the next couple of months your life will totally change and you've got to start preparing for it now.

It's important to take things easy, especially if you are not sleeping well. Your body is going through a lot of physical stress and needs to be looked after, so rest as much as you can. But try to get out every day too. A daily walk is good exercise; it will benefit your circulation and general health. Don't go too fast or too far or the exertion may

See Weeks 27 and 28 for Shopping for Equipment

See Week 33 for Shopping for Layette

Using the time
It's worth stocking up on non-perishable items now, because you won't be able to get out for a major shopping trip for quite a while with a newborn baby.

If you haven't already finished work, you should soon be doing so, and this is the time to start planning for labour and your new family life. Your mind may be reeling with conflicting emotions: you're probably excited at the prospect of your baby being born – and yet unable to really imagine having a baby; you may be nervous about the birth itself and worried about whether your baby is going to be all right. At the same time you may even feel unsure about whether you really want a baby! The only sure thing is

Tips for travelling
☐ Don't stray too far from home in the last few weeks in case labour begins.
☐ When travelling as a passenger in the car, you may find you have more space in the back seat.
☐ Stop every hour or so on a car journey and go for a short walk.
☐ Always take plenty to drink on a journey as you may well get thirsty.
☐ Remember you may need a letter from your doctor before you are allowed to travel by plane. Many airlines may not let you fly from now on, even with your doctor's permission (see Week 15).

make you exhausted and breathless.

On the practical level, you must get organized. Don't worry about the housework if you don't feel like doing it, but do get ready for the birth during the next few weeks. Pack your suitcase for hospital; finish preparing your baby's room and make sure you have all the equipment and clothes you will need for him immediately. It is also a good idea to spend some time stocking your freezer, if you have one. Cook and freeze as much as you can now for the week immediately after coming out of hospital when you won't feel like cooking, and will not have much time for it anyway.

Use this time to educate yourself too. Friends with babies will be happy to tell you what they can about looking after children. Ask their advice and get as many hints as you can. It's also useful to watch other mothers with their children and see what you think; it will help you to work out what kind of a mother you want to be with your child. Buy a book about child care to read now and to consult in future.

On the fun side, make the most of these last days of freedom. Visit friends or have them round to lunch or dinner. Go to the theatre and cinema and make any frivolous shopping trips now, before you get too tired and shopping becomes a chore.

Week 33

MON

TUES

WED

THURS

FRI

SAT

SUN

Notes

YOU AND YOUR DEVELOPING BABY

You You may well find yourself becoming curious about other babies. If you have any friends who have just had a baby, visit them and watch a newborn baby's kicking movements. You may be able to match the movements to those you are feeling in your womb.

If you want to breast-feed, start giving your nipples a gentle massage daily. If you have inverted nipples and are worried about future breast-feeding problems, you could try wearing nipple shields for a few hours a day. But most problems will be sorted out by a hungry baby.

If you have difficulty breathing, remember to sit and stand up straight. From around Week 36 this problem should disappear as your baby's head will become 'engaged' (descend into your pelvis).

Baby By now your baby will measure about 42cm (1ft 4½in) and will weigh approximately 2kg (4½lb).

On your doctor's notes you will be able to see which way up your baby is (which way he is 'presenting' – see Understanding your Hospital Notes, page 88). He is most likely to have settled into a head downwards position, ready to be born head first. A minority of babies have their bottom downwards, known as breech position.

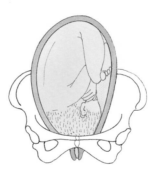

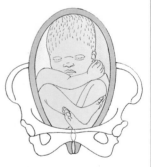

The normal position for delivery is head first.

Some babies are in a breech position, presenting bottom first.

DON'T FORGET Stand up straight at all times and rest for at least an hour a day if you can.

Shopping for layette

Buy just enough clothes in advance to make sure your baby can always be warm and clean over the first few weeks. Remember that babies grow quickly during the first few weeks and months, so don't buy too many of the first size(s). Bear in mind that a new baby doesn't need different clothes for day and night. The hospital may provide clothes for your baby's stay there.

Avoid buying synthetic fabrics for your baby's first weeks. They tend to increase the heat in hot weather and leave him cold when it's chilly. Avoid or remove drawstrings around the neck and make sure that any elastic is not too tight.

Baby toiletries and other items

☐ Zinc and castor oil cream, petroleum jelly or another nappy rash cream.

☐ Soft hairbrush; blunt-ended nail scissors.

☐ Baby lotion for cleaning baby's bottom, useful when you are out visiting.

☐ Pure baby soap or bath liquid.

☐ Changing bag to carry nappy equipment around in.

☐ Cotton wool rolls or balls.

☐ 2 soft facecloths or natural sponges and 2 soft towels: keep them for baby's use only.

Which nappies?

Disposable nappies are more convenient but work out more expensive than washable ones though with washable nappies the initial outlay is high. You'll need 24–30 towelling nappies; disposable nappy liners; nappy pins; 3 pairs waterproof pants; plastic bucket and sterilizing powder or liquid.

Large economy-size packs of disposable nappies work out cheapest, but don't stock up on too many in the small size.

See Weeks 27 and 28 for Shopping for Equipment

First baby clothes

☐ 4 all-in-one stretch suits; buy them with poppers around the inside leg so that you don't have to remove the whole outfit for nappy changing. You can cut off the feet when baby has grown. Or buy nighties instead.

☐ 4 nighties: if you use nighties, buy them with a wide opening.

☐ 4 vests: choose cotton or thermal according to the season; an envelope neck or wrap-around style facilitates dressing. Bodysuits which fasten between his legs don't leave a gap around the tummy.

☐ 3 cardigans/matinee jackets: wool is most comfortable and several light layers are better than one thick one.

☐ 2 pairs mittens: for cold weather. Cotton mittens will stop a young baby scratching his face.

☐ 3 pairs bootees or socks: babies' circulation is poor and their feet get cold through not moving around. Bootees are unnecessary over stretch suits and for summer babies.

☐ 2 bonnets: essential for cold weather. Babies lose most heat through their head.

☐ Sunhat: to protect a summer baby's head and eyes from the sun.

☐ 4 bibs: bibs protect his clothes in case he brings back milk.

☐ Shawl or blanket.

☐ Nappies (see above).

Week 34

Month:

Dates:

MON

TUES

WED

THURS

FRI

SAT

SUN

Notes

YOU AND YOUR DEVELOPING BABY

You You may now start to notice Braxton Hicks contractions beginning. They will feel like a 20–30-second hardening of your uterus and they usually occur during the last weeks of pregnancy if not before. These contractions are sometimes wrongly interpreted as signs of premature labour. Although uncomfortable, they are not painful; they are weaker and last less time than labour contractions.

Baby Your baby's skin is becoming pinker. He is beginning to be able to differentiate between light and dark and, for example, is able to see more if the sun shines on your stomach. He is also blinking.

During the first stage of labour your cervix (2), normally closed, starts to thin out and to dilate, or open. The contractions of the uterus (1) gradually draw the cervix upwards, over the baby's head.

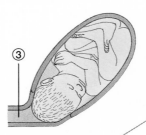

The dilatation of the cervix is measured in centimetres. At 5–6cm (2–2⅜in) you are approximately half-dilated. The baby's head is being squeezed lower in the uterus.

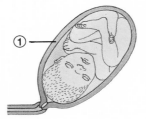

At 10cm (4in) the cervix is fully dilated. It has stretched open sufficiently to allow the baby's head to pass through the vagina (3).

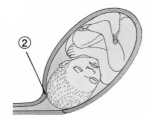

DON'T FORGET Start arranging friends, relations or paid help to come in and help you after your baby is born.

Breathing for labour

because this is what relaxes you. The inward breath will always take care of itself. Do not hold your breath at any stage, as this increases tension. Breathe as deeply as is comfortable; you will find that your breathing is quite shallow when practising at home, because you are still, but be prepared for it to get deeper in labour when you are working much harder.

Breathe in through your nose and out

See Week 29 for Learning Relaxation

See Week 37 for Onset of Labour

> **Breathing techniques**
> Breathe in through your nose and out through your mouth. Remember to breathe as smoothly as possible and as deeply as you find comfortable, concentrating on the outward breath.

Controlled breathing will help you to cope with your contractions by encouraging you to relax your muscles and by distracting your mind and body from any pain you may experience. If you go to antenatal classes you will be taught some breathing exercises and it is a good idea to practise them at home on a regular basis. During these exercises your mind should be concentrating and your body should be completely relaxed. It might help your mind to concentrate if you fix your eyes on an object in the room.

The particular exercises may vary slightly from one hospital, or antenatal class, to another but the principle of breathing for labour remains the same. In some ways, the simpler the breathing the better, because if there are too many different 'levels' to remember you are more likely to become muddled during labour, which may make you feel you have lost control.

Aim to slow down your breathing, and learn to concentrate on the outward breath

through your mouth, pursing your lips. This may seem strange when you are sitting at home, not needing to take large breaths, but will make more sense in labour when your breathing is deeper and faster. But it will take some practice.

So – take a breath in through your nose and try to make the air go down to the bottom of your lungs at the base of your ribs. If you are doing this correctly, you will find that your chest moves only a little but your abdomen is pushed out as you breathe in – put one hand on your chest and the other on your stomach to check this.

As you breathe out, relax those tense muscles – drop your shoulders and jaw and unclench your hands. If you find it difficult to release the tension that is naturally building up, stretch down your shoulders and stretch out your hands to unclench your tensed muscles. In labour, once the contraction is finished, breathe a deep sigh of relief – the pain has gone for a few minutes.

If you become breathless during your exercises, you are breathing too fast – make a conscious effort to slow down. If you become dizzy, it means that you are breathing in too strongly (hyperventilating): cup your hands tightly round your mouth and breathe normally in and out several times until you feel better. Then carry on with the exercises, making the 'out' breath even stronger.

Week 35

Month: Dates:

MON

TUES

WED

THURS

FRI

SAT

SUN

Notes

YOU AND YOUR DEVELOPING BABY

You You will need to buy three nursing bras soon, if you plan to breast-feed your baby. Have them expertly fitted as your body will be changing shape yet again. Make sure they support your breasts and that you can open (and close) each side using one hand only.

Don't stand or sit in one position for too long; not only may your ankles swell, but your body may become increasingly immobile. Rest as much of the day as you feel like.

Baby Your baby is rapidly losing his wrinkled appearance and becoming plumper. Between now and birth more fat will be deposited all over his body, mainly around the shoulders.

The hair on his head is growing and his soft toe- and fingernails have grown almost to the ends of his fingers and toes.

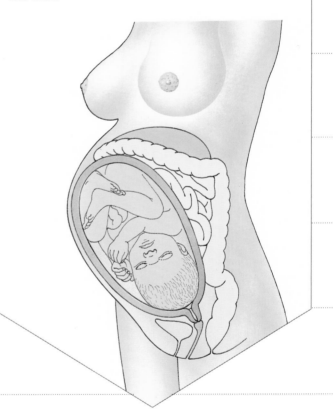

Pain relief

Labour is usually painful, to a greater or lesser degree, therefore it's a good idea to know what kinds of pain relief are readily available so you can think about, and discuss them before it all starts. However, you should always be prepared to be flexible about any decisions you make. Whatever you imagine your labour will be like, it is bound to be different in some respect. Remember that it is not a sin to change your mind.

The relaxation and breathing techniques you have learned will help you in the first stage of labour. Having your partner there to massage you or just hold your hand will also give you reassurance.

Gas and oxygen
This is a mixture of oxygen and nitrous oxide. You breathe it in through a face mask which covers your mouth and nose. It takes fifteen seconds or so to work, so you start inhaling at the start of each contraction. It's easy to use and has no side-effects on your baby. Being self-administered, it also leaves you in control of your own pain relief. Though it lessens the pain it does not remove it completely; if your contractions become very painful you may feel it isn't quite enough and it might just leave you feeling sick, tired and somewhat dispirited. You might then feel this is the time to ask for something stronger.

Pethidine
Pethidine is the most widely used injected drug. It takes about twenty minutes to work and the effects last for two to four hours. You may find it helps with the pain but injected drugs can make you feel, or even be, sick. Or they may make you very sleepy so that you can't push effectively when you need to. There are no serious side-effects, but a drug like pethidine can make your baby sleepy and slow to start breathing if you are given it too near the time of delivery. But these problems will be dealt with in hospital.

Epidural
For most women an epidural gives complete pain relief and for a long or very painful labour it may be an ideal solution. It is a special type of local anaesthetic that works by blocking the nerves which carry the feelings of pain from your uterus, cervix and vagina to your brain. It can even be used for a Caesarean section, allowing the mother to remain conscious for the birth.

The disadvantage of an epidural is that your legs and the lower half of your body are numb and you can no longer move about, or even change position, without help. Since you cannot feel your contractions you may not feel the urge to push either and will have to be told when to do so. This may mean it takes longer to push your baby out or that the baby has to be delivered by forceps.

See Week 34 for Breathing for Labour

See Week 40 for The Birth

Having an epidural
If you know in advance that you want an epidural it is a good idea to ask as soon as you get into the labour room as the anaesthetist may be in demand around the hospital.

Having an epidural is not painful, as your back is numbed before it is given. You lie curled up on your side on the edge of the bed and a needle is injected between the bones of your spine. A plastic tube is threaded down the needle into a place outside the nerves of the spinal cord. The needle is then removed and the tube is held in place on your back by some sticky tape. The anaesthetic is then injected down the tube and takes about fifteen minutes to work. When it starts wearing off, between one and three hours later, further injections are given in the same way.

Week 36

Month: .... Dates: ....

MON

TUES

WED

THURS

FRI

SAT

SUN

Notes

You   The top of your uterus has reached its highest point by now – just below your breast bone. This will make breathing uncomfortable and may also give you a jabbing pain in your ribcage.

If this is your first baby, 'lightening' may occur some time during the next few weeks. This is when your baby's head 'engages', or drops into your pelvis, which indicates that he can pass through your pelvic cavity without difficulty. With a second or subsequent pregnancy, lightening may not occur until just before labour begins. Antenatal visits are weekly from now on.

Baby   All your baby's organs are now almost mature and if he is born he has a ninety per cent chance of survival. Only his lungs may be insufficiently developed. His skin is soft and smooth and his body has fattened out.

Your baby's head has dropped into your pelvis.

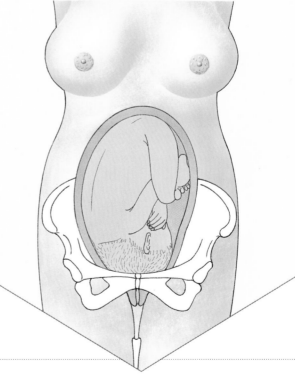

■ **DON'T FORGET** Pack your cases now.

Packing your case

You will need to pack one bag solely for the labour ward, containing all the equipment you might need during labour. It should be ready several weeks before your due date. Some of the items in it will need to go to the maternity ward with you, others can be taken home by your partner. Some items, such as ice cubes, can only be packed at the last minute.

The amount of luggage you take to the maternity ward will depend on the length of your hospital stay. Bear in mind that you can always ask your partner or visiting family and friends to bring in anything you have forgotten, especially consumables like biscuits and fresh fruit. Many hospitals like to keep babies in hospital clothes while they are there, so you may not need any baby clothes until the day you leave. The hospital will also provide a supply of baby toiletries, such as cotton wool, nappy cream and possibly nappies too.

You might think it worth also packing a case now for your partner to bring in when it is time for you to come home. This should contain some comfortable clothes for you (bearing in mind your figure will not be back to its original shape). The baby's clothes could be placed in a carrycot or Moses basket prepared with sheets and blankets.

See
Week 33 for
Shopping for
Layette

See
Week 38 for
Fathers in
Labour

Labour ward bag
- ☐ Mineral water atomizer, plant spray or flannel to cool you down.
- ☐ Vacuum flask filled with ice cubes for you to suck or to use as a cold-pack for backache during contractions.
- ☐ Warm socks (you may get cold during labour).
- ☐ Lip salve or petroleum jelly.
- ☐ Towel and toilet bag containing flannel, toothbrush and other essential toiletries.
- ☐ Hairbrush or comb; elastic to tie back long hair.
- ☐ A mirror (if you want to watch the birth).
- ☐ Nourishing snacks (sandwiches, nuts, raisins, chocolate) to sustain your partner during a long labour.
- ☐ Glucose tablets to give you strength during the first stage.
- ☐ Radio, personal stereo or portable television if they will help you relax; find out if they are allowed in the labour room.
- ☐ Crosswords, playing cards etc.
- ☐ Camera (if you want your partner to photograph the birth).
- ☐ A comfortable cotton nightdress (front-fastening if you plan to breast-feed).
- ☐ Nursing bra; cotton or paper knickers.
- ☐ Coins for the telephone box.

Maternity ward case
- ☐ 2 extra nightdresses.
- ☐ Slippers, bedjacket and dressing gown.
- ☐ Address book, writing paper and pen.
- ☐ 2 packs stick-on sanitary towels.
- ☐ Another flannel (use one on each breast in a hot bath to relieve engorged breasts).
- ☐ Earplugs and eyeshades to help you sleep.
- ☐ Other toiletries such as shampoo, soap, deodorant, face creams and make-up.
- ☐ Tissues and/or soft toilet paper.
- ☐ Can of nipple spray or a tube of cream to help with sore nipples.
- ☐ 2 extra nursing bras; breast pads.
- ☐ Rubber ring (to sit on if you have an episiotomy).
- ☐ Drinks for you and your guests, such as apple or blackcurrant juice.
- ☐ A book to help you relax (possibly one on baby names if you haven't decided yet).
- ☐ Cooking salt (put a handful in each bath to help heal stitches).
- ☐ Nappies. (Check with the hospital if you are expected to bring your own).

Week 37

Month: _____   Dates: _____

MON

TUES

WED

THURS

FRI

SAT

SUN

Notes

GET READY NOW

Although it would be most convenient if your baby was born the day he was due, this is unlikely to be the case. He could be born any day from now until the end of Week 42. The average duration of a twin pregnancy is only 37 weeks so prepare yourself now if they haven't yet appeared. Second, third and fourth babies are also more often early than late.

☐ If you have a family, finalize all arrangements for your children to be cared for while you're away.

☐ Make sure you know where your partner is at all times — ask him to leave all his telephone numbers with you. You could even fit him out with a bleeper, for hire by the week from British Telecom.

☐ Keep your car filled with petrol and put a rug in the back for comfort on the journey to hospital. If you plan to go by taxi, keep the telephone numbers of at least two 24-hour taxi companies by your phone and some money in your purse for the fare.

☐ If you haven't done so, pack all your cases now.

☐ Get your baby's room, layette and crib ready. Make sure his room is clear of rubbish and that it can be made warm the moment he comes home.

☐ Ask at least four neighbours if you can call on them to take you to hospital should you need to go when your partner's not around.

Important telephone numbers

Partner at work:	Neighbours:
Doctor's surgery:	Your parents:
Midwife/Hospital:	Partner's parents:
Note down also your hospital number	Local ambulance:
	Taxi/minicab:

DON'T FORGET If you're at all worried, call the hospital: better to be safe than sorry.

Onset of labour

Even though you may not believe this now, you *will* probably know when you are in labour. There's no point having sleepless nights worrying over whether tonight is going to be the night. No one has ever had a baby in their sleep. You'll be woken up if anything is about to happen, and, if it's not, you need to get all the rest you can to keep you as fit as possible for the actual day.

The most obvious 'signs' to watch out for are described below and one or more of them will indicate that labour has started. However, you may not have any such definite signs. Should you experience any of the three sensations listed below, or if you are at any time worried, call your hospital (or midwife, if you're having a home birth) and tell them. Don't worry that you might be raising a false alarm: doctors are used to this. Any doctor would prefer to check and see whether you are in labour, even if you are subsequently sent home, than have you delivered into his or her safe hands too late.

Contractions The muscles of your womb will start to tighten up and will feel rather like bad period pains or a fist clenching. This is a labour contraction and it will feel quite different (stronger and more pronounced) from the Braxton Hicks contractions that have taken place throughout your pregnancy. The contractions may be accompanied by backache, nausea, wind or diarrhoea.

When these contractions come strongly and regularly, labour has definitely started. Time the spaces between your contractions and when they are coming about every ten minutes, or earlier if you can't cope any longer, telephone the hospital (or your midwife if you are having a home birth).

With a second or subsequent baby, contractions are likely to remain quite mild and infrequent until labour is advanced. They can then suddenly change to long, strong contractions, so don't delay calling the hospital.

A 'show' This is when the plug of mucus at the cervix (neck of the uterus) comes away as the uterus starts to open. You may notice a small discharge of blood-streaked jelly when you go to the lavatory. Telephone the hospital, tell them that you have had a 'show', and they will tell you what to do.

Rupturing of the membranes This is when the bag of amniotic fluid in which your baby was floating breaks and the amniotic fluid starts to come out. It is known as 'the waters breaking'. This usually happens towards the end of the first stage of labour but may happen at the onset of labour or several days before. You'll notice either a small leak or a gush of warm fluid escaping from your vagina. It may feel like a period starting and it may be accompanied by some bleeding. Telephone the hospital at once.

See Week 36 for Packing Your Case

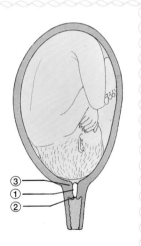

The sticky plug of mucus (1) that seals the cervical canal (2) during pregnancy is dislodged once the cervix (3) begins to dilate. The slightly blood-stained, jelly-like discharge is known as 'the show' when it is released. It may not mean that labour has started, although it indicates that your cervix is opening a little. It may not be dislodged until labour is well under way.

Telephone the hospital immediately if...
☐ Your waters break.
☐ You have any bleeding. If you are bleeding heavily, rest with your feet up until an ambulance arrives.
☐ Your contractions are coming every ten minutes and your waters break.
☐ Your contractions are coming more frequently than every ten minutes or are painful.

Remember to allow for the time it will take to get you to hospital, so don't delay telephoning the hospital for too long. Tell your partner not to drive too fast to hospital: a nerve-racking, bumpy ride can have a worse effect on you than simply arriving at the hospital a few minutes later.

Week 38

Month: Dates:

MON

TUES

WED

THURS

FRI

SAT

SUN

Notes

YOU AND YOUR DEVELOPING BABY

You You may feel bulky and a little bored with your pregnancy by now, or may be getting depressed about having your baby. Rest, carry on taking gentle exercise, have your hair cut and go to the cinema in order to distract yourself. Don't be alarmed by any shooting pains in your groin and down your legs – they are perfectly normal. It probably means that your baby's head has engaged and is moving against your pelvic floor muscles or resting on a nerve. On the whole, however, he is probably moving about less.

Baby The fine lanugo hair covering your baby's body will begin to disappear, although some may remain on his shoulders and in the creases of his body.

Your baby may be trying to breathe, to practise using his lungs, and as there is no air available, he swallows amniotic fluid into his windpipe, which gives him hiccups.

Your baby may be putting on up to 28g (1oz) a day in weight, but your weight will probably remain steady from now on.

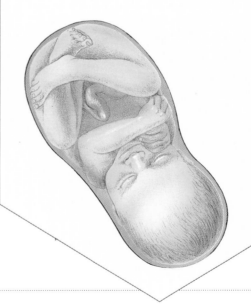

DON'T FORGET Look at these pages with your partner.

Fathers in labour

Labour is one of the hardest, most emotional and most painful experiences you will go through together. Labour itself, and the way you will feel during it, are totally unpredictable for both of you. At worst you will snap at your partner, tell him you hate him being there, scream when he touches you – and bellow at him to shut up when he asks you how he can help. At some stage you are bound to tell him you'll never have another child, and – at that moment – you will mean it! To prepare your partner for your (and his) unpredictability, ask him to read this:

Fathers, be prepared for all of this and don't hold it against your partner. Instead, support her and tell her she is being very brave. Your presence will be invaluable if you can just second-guess what she wants. Make yourself invisible when she doesn't need you.

Remember that you are on the same side. You both want the same results. Respect

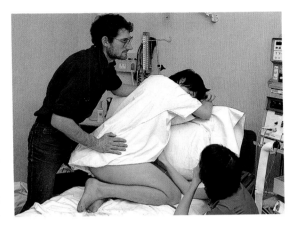

See Week 23 for The Father's Role

See Week 36 for Packing Your Case

your partner's wishes and allow that she may change her mind. You're not experiencing the pain – she is. If she now wants an epidural having talked about 'natural birth', that's fine. Give comfort in any way you can.

Hints for labour partners

☐ Your role will begin the moment your partner starts labour (make sure you know what the signs are, see Week 37). It is especially important *before* you get to hospital, when there is no one else around. Work through her relaxation and breathing techniques now, before labour proper.

☐ Do not try to plan ahead too much or to anticipate events, because labour can take any shape or form. Keep an open mind and remember that there is no 'right' or 'wrong'.

☐ No matter how useless you may feel at some points during labour, be reassured that your very presence is supportive. Yours is a familiar face in a strange atmosphere and that will be comforting in itself. If your partner is unhappy about something, she can turn to you and you can do something about it. If she is confined to bed, you can be her legs and voice.

☐ During her contractions you can 'breathe' with her, especially if you see she's getting in a muddle and needs reinforcement. In the early stages, you can walk around with her and let her lean against you.

☐ Make sure she is well supported and relaxed at all times. During labour see that she has enough pillows behind her, and stroke her if it would help. She may like you to apply a gentle fingertip massage to her tummy, thighs or shoulders. But don't feel rejected if she wants to be left alone.

☐ Always be relaxed yourself. It may be enough for you to just sit in the corner of the room reading or doing a crossword. Ask the midwife if there's anything you could be doing to help.

☐ During labour if your partner says she is in pain, agree with her. Don't pretend the pain isn't there – you are downgrading her experience. Instead, congratulate her on how well she is doing.

☐ If you are asked to leave the room because the doctor or midwife wants to examine your partner in private, make sure *she* wants you to leave. If she doesn't, courteously ask if you can stay.

☐ Giving birth is a highly emotional state. Don't be surprised if your partner gets upset and if you, too, find yourself slightly overwhelmed and disturbed emotionally.

Week 39

Month: _____ Dates: _____

MON

TUES

WED

THURS

FRI

SAT

SUN

Notes

YOU AND YOUR DEVELOPING BABY

You If this is your first baby, your womb will now be approximately three fingers below your breast bone — as in Week 32 — if lightening has occurred.

You will probably be feeling quite exhausted by now and may just want to stay at home with your feet up. Do just that — rest is essential. If, however, your 'nesting instinct' makes you want to rush around organizing and tidying everything up, that's all right too — but don't take on too much and don't strain or stretch your body.

Baby Your baby's intestine is filled with meconium, a sticky, dark greenish-black substance made up of the excretions from his alimentary glands mixed with bile pigment, lanugo and cells from the bowel wall. This will be his first motion, which will be passed during the first two days of his life, and possibly also during labour, so don't get a shock when you see it.

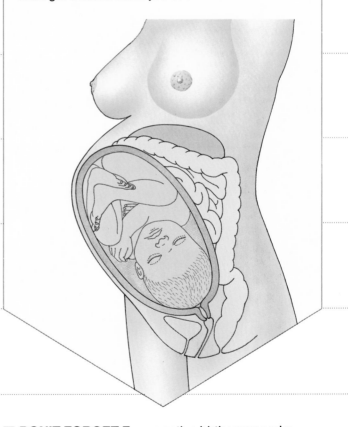

DON'T FORGET For an active birth you need a support partner or two.

Positions during labour

There are as many different labour positions as there are women, so it's important to get your body into some of them now to see which feel comfortable. At the time you will rely more on instinct to choose the right one. No matter which birthing position you choose, it is important to give your baby as much room as possible. This can be achieved by holding your knees well apart and allowing your uterus to tilt forward on to your abdominal wall, away from your spine.

Some hospitals prefer women in labour to be lying down, though many now have a more open-minded attitude. You may feel you want a more active labour, during which you stand, sit, kneel, rock, walk about or squat. Bear in mind that an active birth means you need a support partner (or two). It also means you can't have an epidural.

If you want an active birth it is important that you discuss your views with the hospital well in advance (see Week 9); you may have to find a hospital that has the facilities for women to be active during labour, such as adjustable beds for birth.

It is imperative that you trust the medical staff who are delivering your baby and co-operate with them. Don't be upset if you end up lying on a hospital bed unable to move, with a fetal scalp monitor on your baby's head or an intravenous drip in your arm. The richness of your labour experience won't be lessened, it will just be different.

See Week 31 for Good Posture

See Week 9 for Antenatal Care

Active Birth? Pros and Cons
- [ ] If you are left to find the position that suits you, your pain may be reduced.
- [ ] Squatting or kneeling puts your pelvis and pelvic organs in the best position to deliver your baby.
- [ ] If you are upright you have the force of gravity on your side.
- [ ] In an upright position your uterus won't press on the large veins leading to the heart, which may give your baby a better chance of getting his oxygen supply.
- [ ] Being upright can promote stronger contractions in the first stage. This may lessen the need for forceps or episiotomy.
- [ ] An upright position allows for spontaneous delivery of the placenta.
- [ ] Lying down may be more restful for you.
- [ ] If you're lying down it's easier for the doctor and midwife to examine you.

The most conventional birthing position in hospital is lying on your back with several pillows under your head, pulling your thighs towards you and pushing your feet against two midwives. ▷

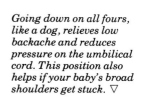

Going down on all fours, like a dog, relieves low backache and reduces pressure on the umbilical cord. This position also helps if your baby's broad shoulders get stuck. ▽

◁ *If contractions are weakening, stand facing a wall with your feet well apart and lean forward, placing your lower arms under your head on the wall. This lets your uterus become as spherical as possible.*

Week 40

MON

TUES

WED

THURS

FRI

SAT

SUN

Notes

YOU AND YOUR DEVELOPING BABY

You You may be getting quite nervous as the expected date of delivery approaches. After all, pregnancy is now quite a familiar state! Only five per cent of babies arrive on their due date, but you may well be one of the lucky ones.

Baby His skin is soft and smooth and most of the lanugo has disappeared. His body is completely covered with vernix.

Don't get a shock when you see him for the first time. He may be blue in colour, some of his head and body will still be covered with white, cheesy-looking vernix, and may also be smeared with your blood. He will be wet and slippery, his hair will have stuck to his face and he will probably be pulling an angry face just before taking his first breath; in addition, his head may still have a strange shape after the passage down the birth canal. Never mind – he's there and he's safe. You won't be looking that great either!

Your fully developed baby is soon to leave your womb.

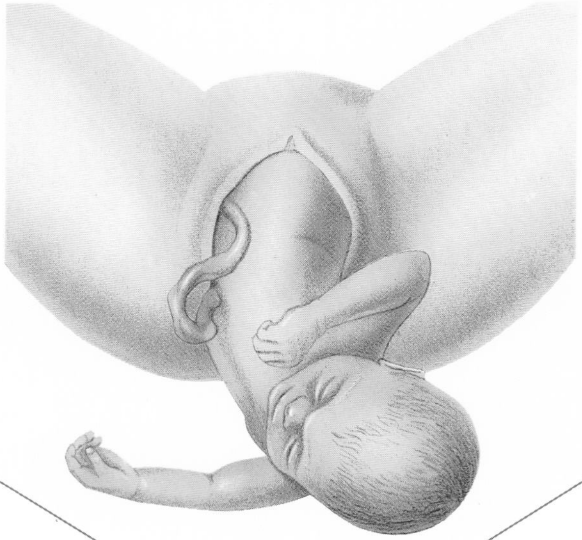

DON'T FORGET Give up all preconceptions, and keep a flexible attitude of mind throughout the birth.

The birth

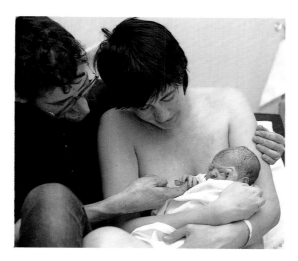

There is no such thing as the perfect birth. Nor is there such a thing as failure in labour, as there is no standard to be achieved. Each labour is highly individual and you should be prepared to work with whatever your own labour brings.

You will have lived through your baby's birth countless times in your mind, but this time it will be for real. It is unlikely to be as you have imagined and, realistically, it may well be worse. Remember that whatever pain you are going through *will* end. There are drugs to help you through it, should you want them. On the day everyone will be on your side, so let them help you. But remember that labour is something *you* are doing.

Tell the hospital staff what kind of labour you are hoping for and listen to their advice as to how to achieve it. Don't be disappointed if you can't have the 'natural' birth you planned for. All births are natural and there is certainly nothing artificial about your baby. Equally, don't feel bad if the 'bonding' with your baby isn't immediate; it may take time to get to know each other.

The first stage

The first stage is when your cervix, which is usually closed, starts to dilate or open up. Your contractions, caused by the muscles of the womb shrinking, will slowly open up your cervix until it is about 10cm (4in) wide and ready to let your baby through.

Concentrate on the relaxation and breathing you learned to do. Take each contraction at a time and don't let anyone or anything interfere with them. Don't feel you need to be polite during a contraction; no one expects you to. In fact shouting or swearing is a good way of releasing tension!

Your contractions will gradually get stronger and more painful and you may start feeling you want to push (this is known as the 'transition' stage). To stop yourself pushing, lift your head and blow out in little puffs of air, or pant, with your mouth, legs and pelvic floor completely relaxed.

You will probably be moving about for most of the first stage. If you have backache, try sitting astride a chair or kneel on all fours.

The second stage

The second stage of labour is when your baby is born. Your cervix should be fully dilated before you start pushing. Keep your chin tucked well down and your mouth closed as you give long, slow pushes. Rest between contractions, to conserve all your energy and strength for the next push.

The third stage

The third stage is the delivery of the placenta. This stage is usually very quick and easy. As your baby is born, you'll probably be given an injection in your thigh to help your womb contract. A final contraction will then push out the placenta. Any necessary stitching up will be done next. This is your first opportunity to see and hold your baby.

Induction

There are many reasons why your labour might have to be started artificially. It could be that you have high blood pressure or diabetes, or your baby is some weeks late.

The most popular method of induction is known as ARM (artificial rupture of the membranes). Your membranes are pierced, allowing some of the amniotic fluid to escape. By altering the pressure in your womb this causes labour to start. Another method is by dripping a synthetic hormone directly into your bloodstream.

See Week 35 for Pain Relief

See Week 37 for Onset of Labour

See page 86 for The Postnatal Ward

See Week 34 for Dilatation of the Cervix

The postnatal ward

Life on the postnatal ward may seem like coming down to earth with a bump after the experience you have just been through, but you have a period of great adjustment ahead and should make the most of these few days in hospital. Use the time to get to know your baby, to learn how to care for him with the help and expertise of the hospital staff. Spend some time looking after yourself too, and catching up on lost sleep.

The hospital environment may be an unfamiliar one, but this will be the only time you can concentrate exclusively on you and your baby without other responsibilities.

Getting to know your baby
In most hospitals the baby is in a cot by your side all the time so you have ample opportunity to get to know each other. Don't worry if you don't feel an immediate 'bond' with your baby – some mothers simply take longer than others to establish that close relationship.

It may come as a bit of a shock that you are expected to look after your baby single-handedly from day one. You are bound to feel unsure about how to handle him and what to do when he cries. But take it gently – trust your instincts and give him lots of cuddles. The hospital staff are there to help and will show you how to change a nappy

and how to bath and 'top and tail' your baby. Don't hesitate to ask them for advice about anything else which may be worrying you. By the time you leave hospital, you will have covered all aspects of your baby's everyday care and you should be feeling a lot more confident.

The hospital routine
Most postnatal wards have a fairly strict routine and you will be expected to fit into it. You may find elements of this difficult, such as the early start to the day, and regulated visiting hours but the routine is designed for the ward to run smoothly. The doctors usually do their rounds in the morning and will check on you and the baby; the afternoons are generally more restful and there is usually a period of enforced quiet – use it!

Life on the postnatal ward may at times seem like being back at school, with communal bathrooms and mealtimes and the general background hubbub. Use the opportunity to discuss your experiences or any anxieties with other new mothers.

Although you may want to share the excitement of your baby with all your friends and family, bear in mind that visitors can be very tiring, especially in the first few days. It is also important to spend some time alone with your partner.

Looking after yourself
Use the time in hospital to get yourself in good condition for your return home. Get as much rest as you can and start your postnatal exercises (see below).

If you have had an exhausting labour, you can ask the hospital staff to look after your baby for the first night so that you can catch up on lost sleep. Nobody will think the worse of you for this; you can always ask to be woken if he needs feeding. On the other hand your emotional 'high' may stop you from sleeping during the first night after delivery – you may still be too excited, or may find yourself re-living the birth every time you close your eyes.

The physical strain of labour may make you ache severely and it may be a great effort to drag yourself to the bathroom for the first day or so. If you had an episiotomy, your stitches may give you pain, or at least discomfort, especially when you sit down; sitting on a rubber ring or an ice pack will help to relieve the pressure. Warm baths and using salt in the bath water will help to heal the stitched area. If you are suffering a lot of discomfort, don't be afraid to ask for painkillers or sleeping pills: they will help you to get through the first day or two, after which you will begin to feel stronger and more comfortable anyway.

You may suffer from constipation for a few days after the birth. This can be aggravated if you are worried about your stitches bursting (which they will not). Drink plenty of liquid, and eat fresh fruit and vegetables and 'roughage' cereals, to ensure that the first bowel movement is soft enough to pass without too much difficulty. If necessary the doctor will suggest some medication.

You will find you bleed quite heavily for a few days after the birth and that you continue to have a brown discharge for several weeks after that. Use sanitary towels and not internal tampons.

Breast-feeding

It can take a few days to get breast-feeding sorted out, and it may be painful at first, but don't be afraid to ask for help from the nurses or midwives on the ward. Your breasts will feel tender and become 'engorged', or rock hard, around the third or fourth day when the milk first comes in. Your nipples may also become sore when your baby first begins to suck. But persevere – all these initial problems will be overcome.

Postnatal blues

You may well feel a bit depressed a few days after your baby is born. The level of hormones present in your bloodstream during pregnancy quickly decreases after the birth and your body has to adjust accordingly.

Whatever happens during your time on the postnatal ward, don't worry or be discouraged when things go wrong. Remind yourself what an emotional and tiring experience you've been through. The next wonder of nature is that in a few months you'll have forgotten almost all of it, as you settle into your new life as a mother. You'll have just one beautiful souvenir – your baby.

Postnatal exercises

There will be an opportunity to start postnatal exercises on the hospital ward. Get along to the class as soon after the birth as you feel able. Strenuous exercises should not be done for at least six weeks after delivery. These include lying on your back and either lifting both legs up and then lowering them, or 'bicycling' with both legs raised.

Most of the exercises can be done in bed or, later on, lying on the floor. Do each one six times, relaxing after each. Continue them for at least six weeks after the birth.

Days 1 and 2 after birth

1. Lie on your back with your legs straight and slightly apart. Bend and stretch your ankles, then your toes, then circle your feet in both directions.
2. Lie on your back with your knees bent and your feet resting on the bed or floor. Tighten your buttock muscles and pull in your abdomen so that your back is pressed against the bed. Hold for six, then relax.

Day 3 after the birth

Introduce the following to the above exercises:
3. Practise your pelvic floor exercise (see Week 17) lying on your bed with knees bent.

Day 4 after the birth

Introduce the following:
4. Lie with your right knee bent and your right foot on the bed and your left leg straight. Slide the heel of your left leg up and down the bed, keeping the leg straight and using only your waist muscles. Change legs.
5. Lie with your knees bent and your feet on the bed. Pull in your abdominal muscles and reach across your body to place one hand on the opposite side of the bed at hip level. Return that hand to its starting position and do the same with the other hand.

Understanding your hospital notes

At your first antenatal visit you will be given a co-operation card which will be filled in at each visit with the results of the routine tests and comments on your and your baby's health and progress. Keep the card with you at all times. If you ever need medical help, all the relevant information is on it.

Most of the abbreviations that you will see on your card are explained below. If there is anything on your card that you do not understand, or if you simply can't read the midwife's writing, ask for it to be explained.

Date
The date of your antenatal visit.

Weeks
The length of your pregnancy in weeks, from the first day of your last menstrual period.

Uterine size/Height of fundus
This is the distance in centimetres from your pelvis to the top of your womb, i.e. the length of your fundus (see Week 20). The figure should be roughly the same as that in the 'Weeks' column.

Urine Alb. Sugar
This shows the result of your urine tests for protein and sugar. 'Tr' or '+' means a trace (or quantity) has been found. 'Alb' stands for albumin, one of the proteins that could be found in your urine. 'Ketones' means you are low in energy. 'NAD', 'Nil', or a tick all mean nothing abnormal discovered.

B.P.
Blood Pressure. This should stay at about the same level throughout pregnancy. If it goes up it can be dangerous for your baby.

Weight
This is your weight in kilograms (see Week 25).

Presentation and position
This shows which way up your baby is lying or 'presenting'. 'Vx' means vertex; 'C' or 'ceph' means cephalic. Both words literally mean the top of the head and show that your baby has settled into a head downwards position and is ready to be born head first. 'Breech' means that your baby has his bottom downwards. 'ECV' (external cephalic version) shows that your baby has been turned round by a doctor pressing on your abdomen so that your baby now has his head downwards for birth. 'PP' means presenting part – the bit of your baby that is coming first.

Up to about Week 30 your baby moves about a lot and then usually settles down. You may find your doctor or midwife only start filling in this column then.

Relation of PP to Brim
This is where your baby's head (the 'presenting part') is situated in relation to the brim of your pelvis. 'E' or 'Eng' means engaged. That is when your baby's head has dropped into your pelvis ready for birth. This may

INVESTIGATIONS	DATE	RESULTS
A.B.O. BLOOD GROUP		
Rhesus Blood Group		
Antibodies		
WR/KAHN		
RUBELLA ANTIBODIES		
AUSTRALIA ANTIGEN		
Cx SMEAR		

DATE	WEEKS	UTERINE SIZE	URINE ALB. SUGAR	B.P.	WEIG Kg
20. 03. 87	13+6		NAD	110/60	80
24.4.87	18+	18	NAD	110/70	81.
21.5.87	22	22	NAD	110/60	82.
18.6.87	26	26	NAD	110/60	83.
29.6.87	28		NAD	110/60	85
3.7.87	30		NAD	110/60	87.
3.8.87	33+		NAD	110/66	91.
4.9.87	37+	37	Kace protein	110/70	9?
18. 9. 87	39+5		NAD	105/70	94

not happen until a few weeks before his birth or not until you are in labour. The engaging of your baby's head is expressed in fifths. So 1/5th means he is beginning to engage, 2/5ths means he has dropped further down and so on. 'NE' means not engaged.

Abbreviations are also used to describe the way your baby is lying in your abdomen. The 'O' stands for occiput (the crown of your baby's head); the 'R' and 'L' for whether the baby is on the right or left side of your body and the 'A' and 'P' for whether your baby's back is facing to the front (anterior) or to the back (posterior) of your body. So 'ROA' means your baby is lying on the right side of your body with his back facing the front.

FH
'FHH', or 'H', or a tick means fetal heart heard. 'FHNH' is fetal heart not heard. 'FMF' is fetal movements felt.

Oedema
This is the swelling, usually of your hands, feet and ankles (see Week 24) which can lead to further problems. '+' means you have oedema and each further '+' denotes the degree of swelling.

Hb
'Hb' stands for haemoglobin. This is tested in your blood to see whether you are anaemic. 'Fe' means that iron has been prescribed.

Next visit
The approximate date of the next visit to your doctor or hospital is written in this column. 4/52 means in four weeks' time, 1/52 means in one week's time and so on.

Sig.
This is where your doctor or consultant puts his initials after giving you your check-up.

ANTE-NATAL RECORD								
	FIRST EXAMINATION		**α FETOPROTEIN**		**FIRST ULTRASOUND EXAMN.**			**SPECIAL POINTS TO WATCH**

DRUGS	FIRST EXAMINATION		α FETOPROTEIN		FIRST ULTRASOUND EXAMN.			SPECIAL POINTS TO WATCH
	Height		SERUM:–		Date: 24·4·87			
	Breasts		Date					
ALLERGIES	Heart			OTHER TESTS	Maturity 18⁺/40			
	Lungs							
	Varicose Veins				Placental Site: ⟋ posterior			
	Pelvis							
					Other Findings FH ✓			

PRESENTA-TION AND POSITION	RELATION OF P.P. TO BRIM	F.H.	OEDEMA	Hb	NEXT VISIT	SIG.	COMMENTS & RESULTS OF ANTENATAL INVESTIGATIONS
			NiL	88	4/52	PCB	
—	—	Scan	NIL	10·9 iron	4/52	CGh	AFP taken
—	—	✓	NIL		4/52	AR	
					4/52	AR	
					4/52	CGh	
Vx					4/52	PCB	
					4/52	Hen	
Ceph	ROA	FHH	+	10·3	2/52	Hen	Head Engaging
Ceph	4/5	H	H		1/52	PCB	

	PLANNED DISCHARGE	POSTNATAL EXAMINATION AND FAMILY PLANNING VISIT
	@ 48 HOURS	BY:
	@ 5 DAYS	HOSPITAL CLINIC
	@ 9 DAYS	FP CLINIC
	@ OTHER	GP

Glossary

Afterbirth
See Placenta

Amniocentesis
A test sometimes performed during pregnancy which is used to detect chromosomal disorders such as Down's syndrome. It is usually done only if it is thought there may be a risk of your child suffering from one of these disorders (see Week 17).

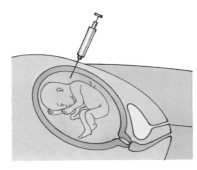

Amniotic sac
Inside your uterus your baby is floating in an oval bag formed of two thin tissues (membranes) called the amniotic sac. It is filled with waters (amniotic fluid) which cushion the baby from any knocks and jolts during pregnancy. Before or during labour, the membranes will break and the amniotic fluid will leak out. This is called 'breaking the waters' (see Week 37).

Analgesia
An analgesic is a pain-easing agent which does not cause unconsciousness. The analgesics that are most commonly used in labour are Entonox (a mixture of nitrous oxide and oxygen, known as 'gas and air') and Pethidine (see Week 35).

Antenatal
Before birth.

Braxton Hicks contractions
These are thought to be the uterus's way of preparing for the contractions of labour (see Contractions). They occur every twenty minutes throughout pregnancy, although you may only notice them during the last few weeks. They feel like a painless but uncomfortable hardening across the stomach (see Week 23).

Breech presentation
Most babies are born head first, that is, the head is the presenting part. A baby in a breech presentation means that his bottom is presenting and he will come out bottom (or, in rare cases, legs) first. Only about three in every hundred babies are breech. If your baby is in a breech presentation your doctor will try and turn him round before birth.

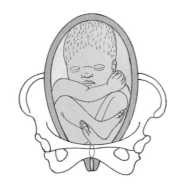

Cervix
This is the neck of your uterus, the bit which looks like the narrow part of the pear (see Uterus). It is 2.5cm (1in) long and when you are not pregnant remains almost completely closed with just a small opening through which blood passes during your monthly period. During labour muscular contractions gradually open up the cervix more and more until it is about 10cm (4in) wide, so that your baby can pass through it, and into your vagina.

Contractions
Regular tightening of the muscles of the uterus. During labour these become more forceful and will push your baby down the birth canal (see also Braxton Hicks contractions).

EDC/EDD
Expected date of confinement/ Expected date of delivery.

Embryo
The embryo is your baby in the early stages of pregnancy. As it grows more like a baby it becomes known as a 'fetus', usually from Week 7.

Engaged
About Week 36 in a first pregnancy (later for second and subsequent pregnancies), your baby's head will drop down (engage) into your pelvis so the widest part of his head is

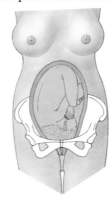

through your pelvic brim. This will make labour easier and will also help you to breathe. Another term for this is 'lightening'.

Most babies are born head first and will have engaged in your pelvis before labour begins.

Epidural
An anaesthetic used in labour to relieve your pain while leaving you fully conscious. It is done by an injection into the fluid surrounding your spinal cord (see Week 35).

Episiotomy
An incision made in your perineum just before your baby is born in order to enlarge the exit for him and to prevent you tearing.

Fallopian tubes
Two narrow tubes about 10cm (4in) long which lead from your ovaries to your uterus.

Fetus
See Embryo

Fundus
The top of your uterus (see Week 20).

Gestation
The period from conception to birth (i.e. nine months).

Hormones
Chemicals produced by the body to perform functions in particular to do with growth and reproduction. They have a variety of effects during pregnancy.

Induction
Any process which starts labour artificially (see Week 40).

Labour
The process of childbirth.

Lanugo
A growth of fine hair which will appear all over your baby's body during pregnancy (see Week 16).

Lightening
See Engaged

Membranes
See Amniotic sac

Miscarriage
The loss of a baby before twenty-eight weeks' gestation. The risk of miscarriage is highest in the first twelve weeks of pregnancy.

Mucus
See Plug of mucus

Ovaries
There are two ovaries (female sex glands) in your body, each of which is about the size of a large almond. Every month one of them expels an egg, or ovum, which weaves its way down the Fallopian tube in search of male sperm on the way up from the vagina.

Perineum
The area between your vagina and anus.

Placenta
An organ grown solely to nourish your baby and to excrete his waste products. It is a more or less circular piece of tissue, attached on the one side to your uterus and on the other to your baby via his umbilical cord. The placenta works like a sieve, allowing oxygen, food and protective antibodies to be passed from you to your baby, but in the same way toxic substances (see Week 2) can be filtered through as well. The placenta also passes your baby's waste products to you for disposal. The placenta, or 'afterbirth', is expelled through the vagina shortly after your baby is born in what is known as the third stage of labour.

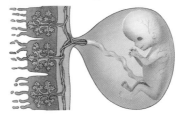

Plug of mucus
Placed in the cervix, like a cork in the neck of a bottle, the plug of mucus seals off the contents of your uterus from outside

91

interference and protects your baby from infection. The plug comes out in order for the waters to break (see Week 37). (See also Amniotic sac)

Primagravida
A woman pregnant for the first time. An 'elderly primagravida', in medical terms, is anyone having a first baby over the age of twenty-five.

Quickening
The first movements of your baby inside the uterus.

Rubella
Another name for German measles (see Week 2).

Scan
See Ultrasound scan

Stillbirth
The delivery of a baby who has already died in the uterus after twenty-eight weeks of pregnancy.

Trimester
Pregnancy is divided into three trimesters (literally thirds of pregnancy). The first is the first thirteen weeks of pregnancy, the second lasts from Week 14 to Week 27 and the third is from Week 28 until delivery (see Week 4).

Ultrasound scan
A highly sophisticated instrument which uses sound-waves to show the development of the baby in your uterus (see Week 16).

Umbilical cord
This is the link between you (your placenta) and your baby. Blood circulates through the cord, carrying oxygen and food to your baby and removing waste. The cord measures about 60cm (2ft). (See also Placenta)

Uterus
Before impregnation your uterus (womb) is about the same shape and size as a small, upside-down pear, weighs about 55g (2oz) and is hollow with a thick muscular wall. At the top it is joined on either side to the Fallopian tubes; the other, narrow end is called the cervix.

When you become pregnant the fertilized egg embeds itself in the lining of the uterus and your unborn baby remains in there until the end of your pregnancy. By the time your baby is fully formed, the uterus is a powerful 0.9kg (2lb) muscle-mass capable of pushing your baby out.

Vagina
Your vagina is a tube of muscle about 8–10cm (3–4in) long which leads from your cervix to your vulva, your external sexual organs. The vagina forms the birth canal during labour.

Womb
See Uterus

When writing for information please enclose a stamped addressed envelope.

ANTENATAL CARE AND BIRTH
Caesarian Support Group
c/o 7 Green Street
Willingham
Cambridgeshire
CB4 5JA
(0954) 60630

Family Planning Information Service
27–35 Mortimer Street
London W1N 7RJ
071-636 7866
Also information about free NHS facilities

Miscarriage Association
18 Stoneybrook Close
West Bretton
Wakefield
West Yorkshire
WF4 4TP
0924-85515

National Childbirth Trust
9 Queensborough Terrace
London W2 3TB
071-221 3833

Royal College of Midwives
15 Mansfield Street
London W1M 0BE
071-580 6523

Society to Support Home Confinements
Lydgate
Wolsingham
County Durham DL13 3HA
0388-528044

Useful addresses

Stillbirth and Neonatal Death Society (SANDS)
28 Portland Place
London W1N 4DE
071-436 5881

West London Birth Centre
7 Waldemar Avenue
London W13 9PZ
081-577 1012
Information and support for those seeking natural childbirth

POSTNATAL SUPPORT
Association for Breastfeeding Mothers
131 Mayow Road
London SE26 4HZ
081-778 4769

Association for Postnatal Illness (APNI)
7 Gowan Avenue
London SW6 6RH
071-731 4867

Down's Children's Association
12 Clapham Common Southside
London SW4 7AA
071-720 0008

Gingerbread
35 Wellington Street
London WC2E 7BN
071-240 0953
Help and advice for single parents

Health Visitors' Association
50 Southwark Street
London SE1 0UN
071-378 7255

Twins Clubs Association
c/o Mrs Dee Hoeseason
54 Broad Lane
Hampton
Middlesex TW12 3BG
A self-help organization to encourage and support parents of twins or more.

SUPPORT AND INFORMATION FOR PARENTS
Compassionate Friends
6 Denmark Street
Bristol BS1 5DQ
0272-292778
Support for families over the death of a child

Cry-sis Support Group
BM-CRYSIS
London WC1N 3XX
071-404 5011
Support for parents of babies who cry excessively

Foundation for the Study of Infant Deaths
15 Belgrave Square
London SW1X 8PS
071-235 1721

National Council for One Parent Families
255 Kentish Town Road
London NW5 2LX
071-267 1361

National Information for Parents of Prematures: Education, Resources and Support (NIPPERS)
c/o The Sam Segal Perinatal Unit
St. Mary's Hospital
Praed Street
London W2 1N
081-992 9310

INFORMATION ON HEALTH, SAFETY AND FIRST AID
British Red Cross Society
9 Grosvenor Crescent
London SW1X 7EJ
071-235 5454

British Standards Institute
2 Park Street
London W1A 2BS
071-629 9000
Publishes leaflets on standards for safe toys and equipment for children

Child Accident Prevention Trust
28 Portland Place
London W1N 4DE
071-636 2545

Health Education Authority (HEA)
78 New Oxford Street
London WC1A 1AH
071-631 0930

RoSPA (Royal Society for the Prevention of Accidents)
Cannon House
The Priory Queensway
Birmingham B4 6BS
021-200 2461

St John Ambulance
1 Grosvenor Crescent
London SW1X 7EF
071-235 5231

Index

A

Abdominal exercises 47
Afterbirth *see* Placenta
Air travel 35, 69
Alarms, baby 59
Alcohol, drinking 9
Amniocentesis 39, 90
Amniotic sac 12, 34, 90
Ankles, swollen 45, 53
Antenatal care 17, 23
Antenatal classes 63
Anxieties 19
ARM (artificial rupture
    of the membranes) 85

B

Baby carriers 61
Backache 67
Back exercises 49
Baths, baby 61
Bed, comfort in 53
Benefits 25
Birth: active 83
    asking questions
        about 23
    fathers' role 81
    see also Labour
Bladder problems 27,
    53
Bleeding 14, 17
    after birth 87
Blood pressure 88
Bottle-feeding 65
Bra: maternity 21, 66
    nursing 65, 74
Brain, development of
    16, 18, 24
Braxton Hicks contrac-
    tions 50, 58, 72, 90
Breast-feeding 65, 70,
    87
Breasts: care of 21, 49
    engorgement of 87
    enlargement of 20, 66
    tender 13, 24
Breathing, controlled
    72
Breathlessness 53
Breech presentation 70,
    88, 90

C

Calcium sources 43
Car, travelling by 35, 69
Carbohydrates 11
Carrycots 61
Carrying 67
Cervix 90
    dilatation of 72
Changing mat 61
Children, other 33
Clothes: baby 71
    maternity 41, 42
Conception 10
Constipation 27, 31
    after birth 87
Contractions 79, 85, 90
Cots and bedding 59
Cramp 27
Cystitis 27

D

Dairy products 11
Depression, postnatal
    87
Diet: healthy 11
    and nausea 19
Dizziness 18, 27
Doctor, first visit to
    16, 17
Douches, vaginal 21, 29
Drugs, taking 9

E

Ears, development of
    18, 20, 24, 26, 34
EDD *see* Estimated
    date of delivery
Emotions 7, 33
Engagement of head
    70, 76, 90–1
Entitlements 25
Epidurals 75
Episiotomy 91
    healing after 31, 87
Estimated date of
    delivery 13
Exercise(s) 22, 47, 49
    pelvic floor 39
    postnatal 87
Exhaustion 13, 25, 29

Eyes, development of
    18, 20, 22, 26, 58, 72

F

Fainting 18, 27
Fallopian tubes 8, 91
Fathers 51, 63, 81
Fats 11
Fears 19
Feet, care of 52
Fertilization 8
Fibre, dietary 11
Fingers, swollen 45, 53
Flatulence 27, 31
Folic acid 43
Food *see* Diet
Frigidity, sexual 17
Fundus, height of 45
Furniture, nursery 57,
    59

G

Gas and oxygen 75
Genital organs,
    development of 20,
    36
German measles 9
Getting up 67
Gingivitis 22, 27
Groin, pains in 53, 80
Gums: bleeding 27
    infection of 21, 22, 27

H

Haemorrhoids *see* Piles
Hair, development of
    32, 34
Hair care 21
Headaches 27
Heart, development of
    16, 18, 20, 32, 50
Heartburn 31, 53
Herbal remedies 31
Hiccups, fetal 50, 68, 80
Hip exercises 47
Holidays 35, 69
Homoeopathy 31
Hormones 6, 17, 19, 91
Hospital: asking about
    23

packing for 77
postnatal ward 86–7

I

Incontinence 53
Indigestion 31, 53
Induction 85
Insomnia 29, 31
Iron 43
Itching 29

K

Kicking, fetal 33, 36

L

Labour: herbal
        remedies 31
    onset of 79
    positions during 83
    stages of 72, 85
Lanugo 36, 66, 80
Layette 71
Legs: exercises for 47
    swollen 45, 53
Lifting 67
'Lightening' 45, 76
Limbs, development of
    20, 22, 26, 32, 52,
    62
Linea nigra 30
Lungs, development of
    24, 56, 66, 68, 76
Lying down 67

M

Meconium 82
Membranes, rupturing
    of 79
Minerals 31, 43
Miscarriage 17, 91
Morning sickness *see*
    Nausea
Moses baskets 59
Motions, baby's 82

N

Nail care 21
Nails, development of
    38
Nappies 71

Nausea 13, 19, 25, 26, 31, 53
Nipples, 'inverted' 40, 70
Nose, blocked 27
Nose bleeds 29
Nursery, preparing 57

O
Oedema 45, 53, 89
Ovulation 8

P
Pain relief 75
Pelvic floor exercises 39
Perineum 91
Pethidine 75
Piles 29, 31
'Pins and needles' 53
Placenta 28, 32, 91
Postnatal blues 87
Posture, good 67
Prams 61
Pre-eclampsia 45
Pregnancy tests 6
Presentation 88
Primagravida 92

Protein 11
Pushchairs 61

Q
Quickening 36, 92

R
Relaxation 63
Rib pain 53, 76
Roughage 11
Rubella see German measles

S
Salt 43
Scan see Ultrasound
Sexual intercourse 17, 53, 68
'Shared care' 17
Shoes 41
'Show', the 79
Sickness see Nausea
Sitting 67
Skin: blotchy 21
    care of 21
    itching 29
Sleepiness 25

Sleeplessness see Insomnia
Slings, baby 61
Smoking 9
Spine, development of 16, 18
Standing 67
Star signs 15
Stillbirth 92
Stitches see Episiotomy
Stretch marks 21
Supplements 43
Sweating 21, 29, 38
Swelling see Oedema
Swimming 22, 49, 62

T
Teeth, care of 21
Thrush 29
Tiredness 13, 25, 29
Travelling 35, 69
Trimesters 5, 13
Tummy exercises 47
Twins 7, 37, 78

U
Ultrasound scans 37

Umbilical cord 16, 24, 28, 92
Underwear 41
Urine test 14
Uterus 92
    size of 45

V
Vagina 92
    discharge from 29, 38
Varicose veins 29, 33
Vegetarians 11, 43
Vernix 48, 66, 84
Vitamins 31, 43
Vomiting see Nausea

W
Waters, breaking 79
Weight gain 28, 55
Work, returning to 25
Working when pregnant 33

X
X-rays 9, 25

Acknowledgments

Author's acknowledgments:
With thanks as always to my husband, Nicholas. Also to Nancy Ward; Dr Elizabeth Jones and her colleagues at the Surgery in St Margarets; the staff at Queen Charlotte's Hospital and my son, Michael, for inspiring me even before he was born.

Conran Octopus wish to thank the following:

For advising on text and illustrations:
Greta Balfour, Professional Officer of the Royal College of Midwives.

For illustrations: Biz Hull, Annabel Milne
For design help: Claire Graham
For taking part in the photography: Olivia James, Sue and Elliot Rosenberg, Dr Sonia Robertson
For jacket photographs: David Grey (front jacket), Guillaume de Faubier/Pix (back jacket)

For their permission to reproduce photographs: 1 Loisjoy Thurston/Bubbles; 2 Claude Gibault/Jerrican; 4 Loisjoy Thurston/Bubbles; 7 Pictor International; 12 CNRI/Science Photo Library; 17 Loisjoy Thurston/Bubbles; 18 Petit Format/Nestlé/Science Photo Library; 21 Christian Moser/Marie Claire; 22 Petit Format/Nestlé/Science Photo Library; 23 Sally & Richard Greenhill; 25 Sandra Lousada/Susan Griggs Agency; 26 from *A Colour Atlas of Life Before Birth* by Marjorie A. England published by Wolfe Publishing; 33 Jennie Woodcock; 35 Pictor International; 36 Petit Format/Nestlé/Science Photo Library; 37, 49 Sally & Richard Greenhill; 50 Lupe Cunha; 51 Loisjoy Thurston/Bubbles; 52 Petit Format/Nestlé/Science Photo Library; 55 Camera Press; 63 Loisjoy Thurston/Bubbles; 69 Tim Woodcock; 73, 81, 85 Sally & Richard Greenhill; 86 David Sutherland/Tony Stone Photo Library.